QUEEN OF THE RIVER

By the same author

SHEEPDOG GLORY

CRAIG OF THE WELSH HILLS

DROVERS HIGHWAY

THE ESCUMINAC DISASTER

ROY SAUNDERS

QUEEN OF THE RIVER

OLDBOURNE
LONDON

OLDBOURNE BOOK CO., LTD.,
121 *Fleet Street, London, E.C.4*

TO MY MOTHER AND FATHER

Set in Janson eleven on fourteen point and printed in Great Britain by Tonbridge Printers Ltd., Peach Hall Works, Tonbridge, Kent.

FOREWORD

It is very gratifying that a British writer of the calibre of Roy Saunders should have been attracted by the story of Canada's Atlantic Salmon. In July 1959 he reached the Fisheries Research Board of Canada's Biological Station at St Andrews, New Brunswick, with a travelling outfit that bespoke a prime interest in the out-of-doors. Besides the clothes he wore with hiking boots and a stout walking-stick, he carried a large haversack containing spare clothing, sleeping bag, note-book, sketch-pad, binoculars and compass. Over several weeks our research activities were shown to him, and he was put in touch with people having varied interests in salmon. Our trips with him were most enjoyable, and we admired his zeal and exceptional ability as a naturalist.

Although the same species of salmon, *Salmo salar*, occurs in Canada and Great Britain, its habits differ in the two areas, related to climate and river conditions. There are also differences in research and management methods, and in descriptive terminology. To obtain material for a book about salmon in six weeks was no mean task, if descriptions of life-history and habits in our waters were to ring true. We offered to read the manuscript before publication, and it reflects well on the author's desire for accuracy that he readily agreed. He has made every effort to comply with our suggestions, and if errors occur we share the responsibility.

Mr Roy Saunders is solely responsible, of course, for conceiving the story with its many absorbing incidents. When he describes incidents on the fictitious Missimi River like 'international poaching,' and refers to forms of wildlife like wolverines that have not been recorded in our Maritime Province for many years, that is his privilege as a novelist.

I believe that this book will give a useful insight into some of the research and management activities now in progress in eastern Canada, aimed at increasing the abundance of salmon and their availability to all groups of fishermen.

C. J. Kerswill,
In charge of Atlantic Salmon Investigations
Fisheries Research Board of Canada
Biological Station, St Andrews, N.B.

CONTENTS

LIST OF ILLUSTRATIONS

ACKNOWLEDGEMENTS

IN writing this story on Canada's Atlantic salmon, I gladly acknowledge the help that was given to me on both sides of the ocean. To the many fishery experts with whom I talked and walked beside the splendid salmon rivers of Canada and Wales I offer my grateful thanks.

To those people who helped in the execution of my quest, this ready co-operation is acknowledged with gratitude.

Gwilym Dunn of Quebec City.

Cornelius Lewis, Builth Wells.

Preston Griffin, Manager of the Miramichi Salmon Anglers Association, N.B.

Douglas Iremonger, Superintendent of the Dee River Board, Chester.

Robert Bourassa, Director of Management and Protection, Department of Fisheries, Quebec.

C. A. Millward, Superintendent of the Wye River Board, Hereford.

Brian Carter, Canadian Fish and Wild Life Service, Nova Scotia.

Selwyn Roderick, B.B.C., Cardiff.

Louis Philippe Gagnon, Superintendent, Department of Fish and Game, Quebec.

Tom Parry, Head Water Bailiff, Dee River Board, Llandrillo, Merioneth.

K. Shillington, The Fish Hatchery, Saint John, N.B.

Morrison Jordan, The Fish Hatchery, Southesk, N.B.

Alex Baxter, Margaree Fish Hatchery, Cape Breton Island, N.S.

Irvine Green, Manager Rocky Brook Fishing Camp, N.B.

T. H. Turner, Director of Information and Educational Service, Department of Fisheries, Ottawa.

W. W. McCormack, Deputy Minister, Department of Lands and Mines, Fredericton.

Arthur Swain, Senior Scientific Officer, Ministry of Agriculture, Fisheries, and Food, London.

Mr John Olin and Col. Weldon of the Ristigouche Club, Matapaedia, Quebec.

Mr Rooney, the Club Manager, and Murray Fraser the Head Guide.

Mr Ralph Burge, The Goldcliff salmon trap, Newport, Mon.

The Chief Supervisor of Fisheries, Halifax, N.S.

The Staff of the Canadian Fisheries Research Boards Biological Station, St Andrews, N.B., including Dr Paul Elson, Dr Miles Keenleyside, Messrs D. Betts, J. MacInerney, K. Sandercock, W. Moss, G. Cooper.

Dr Roscoe Howells, Chief Fisheries Officer, South West Wales River Board.

The Fraser Pulp and Paper Co.

The International Pulp and Paper Co.

To the guides, scientists, hunters, cooks, trappers, poachers, wardens, lumberjacks, forest fire watchers, and anglers of that wonderland of wild Canada, who helped me on the road, my grateful thanks.

But most of all my thanks to my father who first awakened in me a sense of appreciation for a salmon river. From him I learnt to recognise something of the wonder and the challenge in the life story of the great Atlantic salmon, king of all the fish that swim.

INTRODUCTION

Armoured in the silver of its ocean coat, the Atlantic salmon's beauty is unrivalled by any living creature. It is powered with a stored vitality that lies beyond our understanding, and inspired with a courage and an urge to reach its mountain spawning bed that is unique. Beauty, vitality, and courage; three qualities that can be recognised by man. But where do these great fish feed in the ocean? What diet gives such infinite vitality? How do they navigate back along their oceanic course to find again the tiny rivers of their birth? These must remain among the most outstanding mysteries that nature still withholds from man. The odds against salmon survival from the egg to maturity, lie somewhere in the region of one in five thousand. These are some of the ingredients of my story.

At the point when these fish leave the ocean perils, where they are hunted by sharks, porpoises, dolphins and seals, and enter the trap-net world of man, they may well be regarded as among nature's greatest masterpieces. Those that escape the estuary nets swim on through the poisons of industrial pollution to begin a hundred mile struggle against cataracts and waterfalls. There is danger from bears, lynx, eagles, ospreys, and man—the greatest killer of all with his gaff, snare, spear, dynamite, and angling lures. Death awaits the unwary salmon at every turn of their epic river journey.

In spite of the immensity of this persecution, and their

steady deterioration in river water, some fish remain there fasting from six to twelve months, and in all that time they rarely consume any food. Fresh-water lice work side by side with parasitic fungus. River water is a foreign element to the adult salmon, but by a strange decree of nature, the most distant and dangerous parts of this water must be its spawning ground. The Atlantic salmon's journey to spawn is an epic of adventure and endeavour unequalled in the world of nature.

When the spawning act is over, the tired Canadian kelts, gaunt shadows of their former selves, weighing slightly over half their original weight, remain under the ice of the frozen rivers. After the break up, they emerge and try to regain the sanctuary of the sea. Some reach their oceanic goal, and even return a second time to spawn in their natal stream. It has been recorded that a salmon has defied the laws of chance by ascending the river for a third run to spawn. One of these rare third spawners forms the subject of this book.

For practical reasons, in presenting the conjectured reactions of this fish, I have told the story as seen through the eyes of a young Canadian naturalist. This is his story and my tribute to the courage of the salmon whose struggle for existence never fails to excite the admiration of those who try to solve the mystery of their lives. The characters in this book are fictional, but nearly all the events described are those witnessed by my own eyes in the rivers of Canada and Wales.

In the Maritime Provinces of Canada in the early 1950s, salmon fishing assumed such importance that fishery scientists were appointed to examine the status and migration of Atlantic salmon. Active research had been carried out since the 1930s, now the work was expanded. Counting fences were erected across selected New Brunswick rivers where the upstream movement of spawners leaving the Gulf of St Lawrence and the seaward migration of young salmon smolts could be observed and recorded.

During the summer of 1959, I visited some of the chief Atlantic salmon rivers in the forests of Quebec, New Brunswick, Nova Scotia and Cape Breton Island. My companions were scientists, fishery wardens, guides, hunters, trappers, and the students who manned the salmon counting fences. I was the guest of millionaires at the Ristigouche Salmon Club. I travelled by canoe for fifty miles along the rapids of the fabulous Restigouche River. Off the Cape Breton Island estuary of the Margaree, I helped the fishermen to row their salmon catches from the long shore trap-nets. I sailed with the salmon drifter fleet at night from the village of Escuminac, and saw the mile long drift-nets come aboard as the aurora borealis faded before the dawn. Disaster struck this small community and having grown to know its inhabitants, I was inspired to record their tragic story.*

At the counting fences I handled and marked many salmon, and at night, for much of the time, slept under the stars within sound of the thunder of those beautiful rivers.

Nearly three thousand miles of ocean separate the rivers of Wales from those of Canada, but the salmon that use them for their nurseries are identical. So too is the outlook of the fishermen. On the banks of the Grand

* *The Escuminac Disaster*, published by Oldbourne Press.

Cascapaedia where it thunders from the Shick Shock Mountains of Gaspé into the Bay of Chaleur, or on the banks of the Wye where it wanders through the hills of Wales, each angler thinks that the sport beyond the ocean is better than his own. If any difference exists, I failed to notice it.

At home in Britain off the Bristol Channel coast of Monmouthshire, I have seen Atlantic salmon caught in the centuries old traps of the Goldcliff putchers. In the autumn I have seen the spawn being taken from living salmon captured in the North Wales Dee. In the following spring I have seen the tiny hatchlings released in the mountain streams of Hirnant and Treweryn. I have marked young salmon smolts on seaward migration down the Usk and Wye. In autumn I have watched the spawning migrants leaping at waterfalls in the tributaries of the Dee, Usk and Towy, and at the coming of winter, seen the jealous rage in the faces of the cock salmon as they intercepted rivals or stimulated hen fish to their spawning.

To have seen and studied these things for the preparation of this book and to have recorded them in my film 'Kingdom of the Salmon,' is to have witnessed the most moving and fascinating wonders in all the realms of nature.

ONE

THE HARVEST OF SPAWN

The long hot Canadian summer ended as the first great autumn gale swept in from the Gulf of St Lawrence; for two days the hills of New Brunswick were deluged with rain until the dried-up river ways of the forest echoed once more to the crashing roar of the long-awaited spate. The great Missimi River that I had loved since boyhood carried its overload of flood water past my village, along the winding estuary, and away to sea where its turgid path was clearly visible as it drifted over the surface of Missimi Bay.

By the following day, the flood level had fallen and in the evening I went down the hill to the long bridge where two netsmen, Alec and Mack Wilson, were leaning over the parapet watching the movement of the dying flood.

Hard bitten, unimaginative, Alec and Mack looked at the salmon with the eyes of fishermen, with their minds on market prices. They were my friends, although our sympathies—so far as the fish were concerned—were at opposite poles. At this time of year salmon would steal in from the ocean along the tidal estuary, passing the village on their way to face the apparent impossibility of swimming against the fierce Missimi rapids, to disperse along the tributaries in the mountains to spawn. Then in the following spring they would return after the break-up of the ice and go back to the ocean feeding ground, to the source of their dynamic energy. My visit to the bridge was to witness the start of the autumn run of salmon. The fishing season was closed and the two old-timers were on the bridge for much the same reason, except they would curse their luck as the fish began to run when the season closed and I rejoiced that the fish were free. Our sympathies were in opposite camps but our mutual interest created a bond between us.

Throughout the summer months, countless legions of Atlantic salmon had been steadily moving southward along the east coast of Newfoundland. Gradually their route curved into an ever more westerly direction to pass the northern tip of Cape Breton Island and enter the Gulf of St Lawrence. As the salmon shoals moved parallel with the coast, they crossed wide streams of fresh water projected by the rivers of New Brunswick far out across the surface of the sea.

The river smells awakened half-forgotten memories in the fish, and as they crossed each floating highway in the sea, many would respond to the water scent and turn away from the great shoal. The full development of their growth was complete; the inevitable summons had come.

Throughout the summer and autumn, salmon had been returning in this way from the secret feeding grounds of the North Atlantic to spawn in the gravel of their natal streams.

Many of these returning migrants had been netted at sea, many more had been trapped along the coast, others had been taken in the estuarial trap-nets, others had won through to the comparative safety of the rivers, only to be grassed by anglers or gaffed by poachers. Comparatively few won through to the shallow gravel flats in the wild spruce glens of the remote interior to dig the redd and bury their spawn to propagate their kind.

Now in September, the netting season was over, and the late running salmon were safe from many of the hazards that had threatened the early comers.

We stood quietly on the bridge, not talking much, when we had our first glimpse of the incoming fish. There was a ring of tense excitement in Mack's voice as he pointed to them:

'There they are.'

The tide had ebbed and in the aftermath of the flood, the water was clear enough to see the first fish in the salmon shoals. They had been in the bay for many weeks awaiting the call in the taste and smell of flood water which lured them on into the narrow shallows to face the dangers and hardships of their freshwater journey to the redds. The spectacle of those leading fish was unforgettable. They moved steadily forward against the current under the spell of their migratory urge. Probably a thousand salmon would pass beneath the bridge that night, and only a small percentage could survive to return to the sea.

'Aye there they go,' Alex said. But there was no ring of excitement in his voice.

'I guess th' old salmon must know we've got the nets up, look at 'em, it's the same agen this year.'

'I reckon so,' replied his brother.

Then followed the annual grouse against the fishery laws that declared an early close season on trap-netting, to allow the autumn run of breeding salmon to pass up river. We were soon discussing whether the fish were able to tell the date of season closure, and if they waited out at sea until they knew it was safe to enter the river.

Throughout the summer season Mack and Alex Wilson had carried out a daily inspection of their licensed trap-net that lay for thirty yards across the current. Owing to the drought that year, the salmon had come in only small numbers, and the catch had been a poor one.

Now that the season was over the great shoals had come again to tantalise the men as they watched and theorised on the craftiness of salmon and stupidity of fishery laws that seemed to be made for anglers at the expense of netsmen.

I took no part in the conversation, I was too intent on watching the cavalcade of nature that moved steadily against the current. Catching salmon meant nothing to me, their flavour, price per pound, even their readiness or reluctance to take a bait was no concern of mine. Throughout boyhood, my chief joy had always been to observe them at the gathering pools or follow them along the time-honoured routes between the rocks, or leaping the splash dams at the lumber camps, and clearing waterfalls until they reached the spawning shallows of the tributary rivers.

My interest in the king of fish stemmed from an appreciation of its beauty and the courage shown in its resolve to overcome all obstacles to reach good spawning water. To me the salmon was the greatest masterpiece in all the world of nature. But side by side with this fascination which the fish held for me, was a desire to probe the secrets of its life.

'I guess old Frazer'll get many of these fish in his hatchery trap up-river tonight,' said Alex. Frazer was responsible for the collection of salmon spawn stripped from the living fish at the government hatchery. 'And I guess that big thirty pounder'll be there'n less'n arf an hour too,' said Mack, pointing to an immensely thick hen salmon of superb proportions. She was little longer than any of the other big fish, but her girth was far greater.

'Found a right good feedin' ground I guess,' replied his brother.

Where in the whole wide realm of the Atlantic Ocean did these salmon feed and reach such great proportions?

'Isn't it strange,' I said, 'when young salmon go to sea after spending two or three years in the river, they don't weigh more than about two ounces. Then, after spending the same time in the sea, they may weigh twenty or thirty pounds.'

But my companions were in no mood to philosophise on problems of natural history on the day when their nets had been removed and the shoals were running.

'What's 'er age, Wayne?' asked the older man with a knowing wink at his netting partner.

'Impossible to tell from here,' I said, 'but if you could get me a couple of her scales I'd soon tell you.'

'Oh, you could, could you now,' he asked. 'Well I only wish I could oblige. But d'you honestly mean to tell me that you could tell the age of that salmon by just looking at her scales?'

'Of course I could—with the help of a microscope,' I said, '. . . done it in school many times. I've told you all this before. Every winter of the salmon's life is recorded by slower growth of rings on every scale on its body, and you just count the number of times where the rings come close together and you have the number of winters spent in the sea.'

The two old timers glanced at each other, I knew that they were not above pulling my leg on occasions, for to them a fish seemed a good subject for a joke. They believed me all right, though they were reluctant to admit it.

In any case, the age of a fish was to them of no real concern, their interest in salmon was how to catch and market them; their living depended on it.

We continued to watch for some time until they could stand it no longer, and they walked away and left me alone, 'wouldn't surprise me if you swam off with 'em,' was Alex's parting remark.

The fish had acclimatised themselves to the fresh water of their new environment, they swam easily against the current, free of the deadly menace of the trap-nets which had caught so many of their predecessors. Had the nets been in position that night, hundreds of the egg-laden fish would have been caught. But instead, through the intervention of the law, the burden of spawn in the heavy bellies of the hens was destined to take its chance against the hazards of the river.

By agreement with Fishery Protection, a net near the the Government hatchery, was allowed to remain after the closure of the season, to catch pregnant fish from which the spawn could be taken for artificial rearing of young salmon. As I left the scene to go home, my thoughts were with the big hen fish which we had seen from the bridge.

In the darkness she moved nearer to the left bank with her companions. Finally she made contact with the meshes of the long arm of the net, she recoiled instantly, and panic surged through the entire school of fish. They tried again, with fins extended, ready for instant flight. The nose of the leader touched the net once more, and the school behind her swirled away to circle and return with heads upstream. The cunning angle at which the leader of the trap had been placed, guided the salmon into a holding pen from where escape was impossible. The ocean wanderers found their route barred in all directions, and quietly accepting the inevitable they lay still in the darkness, heads upstream and fins gently moving to maintain position.

During this enforced rest, they had time to smell and taste the scents and flavours of their new environment. Three years had passed since they had left this river of their birth, and their journeyings had taken them to the remote northern feeding grounds of the Atlantic Ocean. Now they were back in their natal stream, and as the current passed them in the darkness, the half remembered scents of the land came to them as they lay. There was the gaseous odour of leaf mould, road tar, earth, mineral salts and the resinous tang from the larch and spruce forests of the watershed, and each smell awakened a distant echo in their memory.

For no living creature are Rupert Brook's words more apt than for the homing salmon:

> 'To smell the thrilling sweet and rotten
> Unforgettable unforgotten river smell.'

With the coming of daylight, human forms appeared against the sky above the fish, and panic came again. Heavy wooden doors in the side of the trap were opened, and the salmon streamed through into a long pool that ended at the hatchery sheds. Fear left them as they merged in the sanctuary of other salmon which had been guided in on previous mornings.

As the autumn days passed, the growing squadrons of silvery prisoners were left in peace until the time came for ultimate capture to extrude the spawn that ripened within them. The blazoning riot of autumn colours burnished the high woods as the maple, poplar, ash and birch turned colour in the fall, and the long pool was carpeted with floating leaves that lent security to the restless fish. In every salmon was the urge to swim on against the gentle current of the water that confined them.

Each night a fresh batch entered the trap, and each morning they were shepherded into the long pool until it presented the spectacle of nearly three thousand salmon with an egg potential which ran into millions.

It was a critical time for Billy Frazer and his men while they waited for the spawn to ripen, for the fish were an irresistible temptation to local poachers. But an intricate system of electric wire fencing had been cunningly arranged between the undergrowth around the pool. If the wire was cut at any point, a siren would sound and flood-lights would be automatically turned on. Frazer took no chances with his valuable breeding haul.

As a shepherd watches the movements of his lambing sheep, so the expert eyes of the hatchery chief watched the behaviour of his fish for the first signs of spawning. Each day the cock salmon grew more restive as they edged rivals away from chosen groups of heavy bellied females. At last Frazer knew that action time had come, and temporary helpers were enlisted. I was soon to leave home to begin a zoology course at Fredericton University, but on the day that stripping began, I drove up the valley to watch. Clad in waterproofs, the hatchery men set about the task of netting groups of salmon in which the spawn was ripe. These were transferred to floating boxes, and carried to the shed for stripping. They were grasped by the tail in one hand, while with the other the belly was pressed until the spawn came away from the vent in a jet of eggs the colour of grated carrot, which were caught in a waiting pan. With about eight hundred eggs to every pound of the fish's weight, three twenty-pounders yielded some forty-eight thousand, as yet, infertile eggs, and the pan was full. Then a hook-jawed cock fish was taken from the box, leaner and uglier than the buxom hens, he was held in the same way over the loaded pan, and a gentle pressure brought a jet of snow-white milt which filtered easily between the eggs. The sperms of the milk penetrated the membranes of the eggs, fertilisation was instantaneous, the shells hardened, and all other sperms were prevented from entering.

The tough Canadian fishery men paid little heed to the miraculous intervention which they had brought about in the process of nature, as they completed the job by gently stirring up the contents of the pan with a feather to ensure the fertilising of every egg. After about eight hours of water hardening they spread them in trays placed inside the shallow troughs where a current of water would wash over them throughout the winter until with the coming of spring they would hatch into tiny salmon fry.

Long hours of hard work continued, and at the end of the day the stripped fish were returned to the river.

The urge to swim upstream had gone, and listlessly they dropped back on the cold November current to the estuary, and beyond to the wide gulf where rejuvenation or death awaited them.

When the last salmon had been relieved of her eggs, and the spawn harvest had been evenly spread about the floors of every trough beneath a gentle flow of water, the doors were closed. Then in the silence of the long and bitter winter, a silence broken only by the gurgling of the well-water that circulated to prevent the growth of fungus on the eggs, the golden harvest of the sea was left to await the touch of spring. Constant vigilance would be maintained throughout the winter when all infertile eggs would be removed as soon as they lost colour and whitened.

With the onset of winter came the first fall of snow, and the sleepy forest bowed in surrender and slept, while overhead long skeins of geese went southward on the night wind. Slowly at first, the rivers froze over and ice thickened until only a shallow stream of water covered the natural spawning beds of the salmon which had missed the net. These fish had moved on far up among the hills to spawn in the gravel under normal conditions. Then with the act accomplished, they would gather for the winter in the gloom of deep pools below the ice and its darkening mantle of snow. The grim Canadian winter claimed both earth and water, and the pulse of life moved ever slower as snow and frost immobilised the forest world.

When at last the dawn of spring came back to the sleeping land, life would move on again, and with its slow return two small black spots—the eyes of the fish—would appear in every egg: The rise in temperature would wake each tiny spark of life, and as the days would pass, the curled-up embryo salmon in the shells would take on the shape of fish and stir spasmodically.

On a day when the ever-climbing sun topped the pines that ringed the dell to bathe the snow-clad sheds with light, the little shells would give way, for the magic moment of release had come after the thermometer on the whitewashed wall recorded 42° for several days and nights. The tiny golden fry would break free in countless thousands throughout the day to lie in inert masses in the passing water, with heads towards the current from the moment of their birth.

If a twenty-pound salmon lays sixteen thousand eggs, and the salmon population remains constant, only two fish from all the eggs of the parents survive to the adult stage. The little salmon's chances of becoming fully grown in the wild are thus reduced to one in eight thousand. But so great is the revenue value from Atlantic salmon angling in the Maritime Provinces of Canada, that the hatchery plan was developed to shield the vulnerable salmon from this wastage. In this way it is hoped to increase the stocks to attract an ever-growing numbers of anglers.

As the eggs hatched, the empty shells would be picked out by the staff. The food supply from the yolk sacs attached to the stomachs would be absorbed into the tiny golden bodies. The instinct for concealment would show itself in the urge to flock together and hide in inert masses of such vast numbers that relays of men would have to stir the water at night to prevent mass suffocation. At first the little fish would be little over half an inch in length, and by about the end of the second week their colour would change from golden orange to yellowish pink. The yolks having been absorbed, the little salmon fry would now be perfect minute fish capable of swimming at great speeds, and ready to meet the dangers of their watery world.

TWO

THE FORBIDDEN FOREST

The harsh Canadian winter passed with interminable slowness until at last the spring gave tongue by avalanches great and small, and throughout the length and breadth of New Brunswick the trees were freed at last of their burden of snow. As the snow slid swishing to the sodden floor of the forest, the branches sprung back in gay relief, and everywhere the dripping woodlands foretold the coming of spring. Ice and melting snow was washed from the whole great watershed of the vast Missimi basin, and the parent river took the burdens of its tributaries as a mother takes the troubles of her family. The debris of winter was slowly washed down to the hungry maw of the sea.

For many days the stately procession of floating ice-floes moved along the curving waterway. The forest trees looked down on the ice that moved in silence, except along the river's edge where the jostling floes bucked and reared over each other and smashed against the tree trunks, tearing bark and sapwood from the sides that faced upstream.

When the floating ice had gone, the bitter wind of spring ruffled the hard blue surface of the river, and the salmon which had stayed throughout the winter in the darkness of the pools, now saw the light of day once more. Some of them had spent six months in the river, and in all that time scarcely a morsel of food had passed their lips. Teeth had disappeared when they left the sea, and intestines had slowly shrunk to make room for the spawn that gradually filled the body cavity. But during the semi-hibernation under the ice, teeth had grown again, stomachs had returned to normal, and the urge to feed came back once more. The mended kelts, or black salmon, moved from the pools to feeding runs and to a rendezvous of which they were yet unaware. Fishermen had to be keen in that fearsome wind to stand in anchored canoes and cast for the salmon as they started on their journey to the sea.

To local anglers who could face the cold, the sport was good, for the kelts were hungry and fought hard when hooked, and their taking was not illegal as in other lands.

Deep in the gravel of the spawning redds the tiny progeny stirred in their shells, broke free, and wriggled upwards through the stones which had held them safe throughout the winter. Famished trout and yearling salmon parr were waiting on the redds to swallow the tiny fry as they broke clear of the gravel, and even as their lives began they died in millions. The slaughter and feasting went on throughout the period of the hatch.

Persephone, the goddess of spring, was moving northward through the forest lands of maritime Canada, and in her wake the wide winged ospreys flew with merganser ducks, bald eagles, and waving pennants of wild geese skeins which spread the music and the news of spring to the waking world. Otters and mink took up the challenge of the opened rivers as the last traces of the ice were swept away.

Then the lumber gangs moved up to the previous summer's cuttings and the pulp drive started as the logs were floated down the rivers to the waiting mills.

Carpets of flowers spread a coverlet of colour over the forest glades, and the singing voices of the migrant birds broke the stillness of the dawns, and the white-tailed deer could taste again the rising sap in the woody stems on which they browsed.

I returned home for a short vacation during May, and on the following day drove over to the hatchery sheds to see the result of the previous autumn stripping.

It was mild in the sheltered dell that led down to the big river, and the first faint scent of spring was there to greet my return to the woodlands that I loved so well. I felt more sensitive to these things after my winter term of study at Fredericton. The main buildings of the hatchery were situated further up the glen, and I went straight to the sheds where the spawn had been spread six months before. I pushed open the door and the clammy coldness of the atmosphere cut my face.

To anyone who has never seen the hatching troughs of a salmon nursery, the spectacle of newly hatched fish is difficult to comprehend. I had seen it many times but, even so, it was always a new revelation.

The long troughs were bursting with life, the water which ran the length of each trough contained a seething brew of living salmon fry. I stirred the water of one trough and a mass of shrimp-like creatures erupted like the dance flight of a myriad gnats, it was so thick that at times it resembled a swirling orange cloud in the water.

Gradually I worked my way to trough Number 27 in which the spawn of the big hen salmon had been spread, and I looked down into an estimated twenty-four thousand wriggling fry vibrant with life. I rested my elbows on the edge of the trough and looked closely into the teeming mass, and recalled the avarice of my two friends on the bridge on the grey September evening as they bemoaned their lost opportunity to catch the mother of that seething cloud of life. As I set up my camera to take a picture of the harvest that had been gathered in that strange way, I visualised the time when a far greater harvest would be gathered from ascending spawners until there would be sufficient salmon fry to plant out in all the tiny rivers of the province where they could grow until they were ready for their journey to the sea. There they could feast and fatten in its infinite bounty and return to the rivers in such numbers that they could be converted into a major food export.

As I was adjusting the camera settings, Billy Frazer arrived with two men.

'How d'ye Wayne,' was his greeting. 'I guess y'er big fish done 'erself proud.'

'She sure has!' I replied.

Then followed the usual inquiries made of a college student on his return home, about his future plans. But being in the atmosphere of salmon culture, I found it hard to discuss such distant realities, and tried to switch Frazer's interest to the job in hand.

'The fry are looking well,' I said.

'Yes, that's so. I guess they've absorbed the yolk sacs now and it's time we started feedin'. We're puttin' 'em in the big tanks today—can you give us a hand?'

'I'd like to,' I replied, 'just give me a few minutes to get a picture.'

In no time at all, my coat was off, I had pulled a thick sweater over my head, donned a pair of rubber trousers, and was ready to help.

Big cans were in position at the end of the first trough, a drain plug was removed and the water and fry poured unceremoniously into the waiting cans. Then they were shifted by truck and trailer to the outside tanks where the fish were to spend the summer.

One by one the hatching troughs were emptied until Number 27 was reached. The plug was removed and the fry poured out in a stream of liquid gold into the waiting can. I watched them go, they would soon be merged with the other countless hosts and their identity for me would be lost.

'Guess I'd like to rear a few of those myself,' I said on a sudden impulse.

'Help yourself lad,' was the reply. I grabbed a jar and held it at the side of the fry-laden jet of water. In this way I acquired a dozen gold orange wrigglers for the purpose of studying their growth. It was a scientific impulse tinctured with a dash of sentiment, for I had known their mother.

When we finished transferring the hatchlings to the long tanks, a liquid paste of crushed liver was sprinkled over the water, and we left them to feed.

I drove home with my baby salmon and fed them on a similar mash of meat tissue, and the golden sprites ate ravenously. Throughout the Easter vacation I kept them in running water to supply the constant source of oxygen which they needed. When I returned to Fredericton I took them with me and they were housed in a glass aquarium in the college laboratory. The orange colour disappeared with the change of food, and they assumed a pale grey which blended with the gravel base in the tank.

Towards the end of that term an advertisement appeared on the common-room notice board. The Canadian Fisheries Research Department invited applications from students for summer vacation work at the newly constructed experimental salmon counting fence at Camp Musquash on the upper Missimi River. An interest in fish was desirable, and ability to live in the isolation of a disused lumber cabin was essential.

Few students were attracted by the prospect of spending the summer in such isolation. Other research posts in connection with caribou, deer counting, fish food, marine biology were more popular. But I applied and was duly appointed to the Camp Musquash project.

On the first day of July, a representative of the Fisheries Board arrived at my home in Missimi Bay with a jeep loaded with provisions, and I was briefed with details of the daily routine for record keeping of salmon movements at the lonely counting fence. When the visitor had gone I was left with the loaded jeep, and I had begun the first stage of the plan of scientific inquiry into the life story of the Atlantic salmon. I fingered the bunch of keys which had been left with me and felt that here maybe were the keys to the solution of the great mystery of the salmon which I longed to unravel. Then I stowed my kit, a rucksack, sleeping bag, binoculars, gun, camera, notebooks, wireless set, and the fish-can containing the twelve growing salmon parr. I roped my fourteen-foot light-weight canoe to the roof, and was ready for the seventy mile drive to the camp.

Access to the little known region of the upper Missimi was only possible by the fifty mile forest road, which

'Five minutes would pass with no movement, then a long dark shape would spring from that seething cauldron, then others would leap in quick succession, as though each salmon waited in the bubbling thunder for a leader to make the first jump.' (*Photo by Arthur Brook. Reproduced by kind permission of the National Museum of Wales*)

A fishway or salmon ladder cut in the rock to enable salmon to negotiate an otherwise impassable barrier. (*The National Film Board of Canada*)

had been privately constructed by Halford's, the pulp and paper organisation who leased large tracts of the Missimi forest for pulp wood cutting. Entry to this road was strictly forbidden except to the lumber crews who journeyed in and out at week-ends. Arrangements had been made between Halford's and the Fisheries Board that I could enter this wild forbidden region in the heart of the province. The dense Canadian bush was a sanctuary of wild life in which I had never previously even hoped to set foot.

Family farewells were taken, and as the jeep started, I knew that a great adventure had begun.

After a twenty-mile drive along the normal paved highway, I came at last to the entrance of the Halford Road. A locked gate carried notices that warned all passing motorists from attempting to enter the forest.

As the jeep stopped before the gate, a keeper emerged from the wooden gate-house and came up to me.

'I guess you must be the guy from Fisheries Department,' he said. 'Reckon you'd best come inside and have a chat.'

I followed the tall, spare figure up the flower-edged pathway and into his wooden house.

'Bit young ain't you, to be goin' t' spend the summer all alone up at Camp Musquash?' he asked.

'Oh, I don't think so,' I replied. 'There's plenty of salmon up there to keep me company and at nineteen I'm probably a lot older than they are!'

The keeper shot me a cold glance over his shoulder. It was a glance so full of suspicion that I regretted my rather smart-alec reply on such a delicate subject as salmon. I was yet to realise that most men who lived in good salmon country were poachers at heart, and that any stranger who mentioned the subject, automatically became suspect. To Bill Machett, gate-keeper of the Halford Road, salmon were there only for one purpose, to be caught, either by the clean skill of angling, or under cover of darkness by net, gaff, or dynamite. There had already been great speculation among the locals, during the building of the counting fence. In spite of the fact that the Fisheries Board had publicised the proposed erection and explained its purpose to the folk who lived in the vicinity, they were slow to realise its significance.

They had seen the loaded government trucks enter the private road, and the story had got round that a giant fish trap was being built in the river, where all salmon were to be caught, marked and then released. It baffled their imagination as to what could be achieved by such a thing, somehow the tale would not 'hold water.' Perhaps this fish lark was all a blind, to mask some sinister development for a rocket station, a secret missile project, or a new atomic power plant. Certainly there were few more remote places anywhere in the wilds of the southern parts of Canada.

Bill Machett had been informed of the arrival date of the operator—myself—and I felt that he had a right to know the full truth from me. He had invited me to his cabin obviously to find out more about it, so I took the initiative.

'Let me tell you about my job up river.'

His face cleared as he led me to the verandah that commanded the entrance to the forest.

'Sit down,' he invited. 'But first I suppose you know the rules laid down by the company. Every time you enter or leave this land you sign the register here.'

I signed my name there and then and the keeper read it.

'O.K. Mr Douglas, have a cigarette.'

'Haven't started smoking yet,' I replied.

'I guess if you'd been a smoker, you'd not have had this job.'

'Why do you say that?' I asked, as the remark seemed curious.

'Well!' he drawled, 'the company don't want no smokers in this forest. Did they offer you a fag before they gave you this job?'

'Yes I guess they did,' I replied.

'Aye, they probably offered all them candidates a smoke and those that took 'em weren't considered. Now get this straight, there's got to be no smoking inside them gates on any account. Weather's turning hot and the woods'll soon be dry as tinder, don't carry matches outside yer cabin, and no fires to be lit at all, and that's an order. If you wander about the woods you've got to keep a log o' yer movements in case o' fire. You know the importance of pulp wood to New Brunswick, so watch it!'

'Yes, that's O.K. I've been told all about that,' I replied rather sharply.

'Who appointed yer?' asked Machett casually.

'Salmon Research Board of the Canadian Fisheries Department,' I told him, and he seemed to be satisfied that I was a responsible person—aside from my age which he clearly seemed to think was too tender for such a lonely existence.

'Now tell me son,' he continued, 'what exactly's yer job up there?'

I tried my best to give him an understandable lecture

on the scientific aspects of the great responsibility which had been entrusted to me. Daily recordings would have to be taken on river level and water temperature; the exact number, sex, and type of salmon that passed the counting fence each day. How all salmon would be marked with numbered tags for future identification. A record had to be kept of all insects hatched over a square yard of average river gravel in each twenty-four hour period. I explained what these investigations would reveal if conducted over a long-term series of experiments. Only in this way could the salmon's life cycle be learned for the benefit of science in particular, and the fishing industry in general.

I saw that Bill Machett was impressed as to the importance of this information to the national benefit of Canada and perhaps the world. He had asked for information, and certainly got more than he could understand, but the main point was that he had at least been satisfied that the much discussed counting fence was after all only concerned with fish. He would now be able to face his curious neighbours and tell them so. But, I reflected, it would be a very garbled version of the scientific fact.

'There seems to be far more to salmon then, than jest catchin' 'em.'

That was Machett's final remark after my lengthy explanation. We both laughed: he had summed-up the situation perfectly!

But Machett was still curious about details.

'You've said plenty about yer job at this countin' fence, can you tell me how it works?' he asked.

'It's very simple,' I said. 'There's a grating of thin iron bars about half an inch apart, running right across the river, not even a smolt can get through. There's only two openings that lead into the two traps, chambers about eight feet square with shallow water running through. As the salmon come up at night they all enter the cage. In the morning I mark them and let 'em out one at a time to carry on upstream. If any smolts are still coming down on their way to sea, they get caught in the downstream trap.'

'Is that right?' said the keeper, with an odd tone of voice.

'How many fish d'ye think you're goin' to find there in the mornings when the Indian poachers get wise to yer idea?'

'The fence is always kept locked,' I assured him. 'It's very strongly made, I've seen all the plans.'

'What if we gets a good flood?' continued Machett.

'It's all weighted down and bolted to the rock, I guess.'

'What about the fishing camp owners?' he pressed, 'those millionaires from the States and Toronto who fly out here for their bit o' fishing. You're goin' to have them up in arms I guess.'

'All been taken care of at headquarters,' I said.

The gate-keeper tried hard to find a weak point in the scheme, but luckily I had been well primed with the main details of the project, and managed to satisfy him on every point he raised.

'Well there's one thing you'll be up agin anyway,' said Machett with an air of satisfaction, 'and that's public opinion, I can tell ye, that's for sure, the people hereabouts don't like it, it's gonna mess up the fish and the fishing, these scientists think they know a lot with all their book learnin', but there's a lot o' things you don't get out o' books I guess.'

'Couldn't agree with you more,' I replied. 'And that's exactly the reason why we've come here with the counting fence, to learn from nature itself. Nearly every new scheme in scientific investigation gets local public opinion against it at the start.'

Bill Machett felt that at least part of the mystery was beginning to clear, and with this enlightenment he would have to be satisfied for it was time for me to leave.

'Let me know how things get on up there when you can,' he said, 'you're on the phone so don't forget to ring, Redhill 45.'

We returned to the gate and he opened it and I started up the jeep turning on to the rough rocky road that I was to follow for fifty cruel jolting miles deep into the green heart of the forest.

The road ran in a straight line between the trees, and climbed steadily. It was a relief to be driving in the shade of the towering woodlands that lined the roadway, in many places their branches met overhead to form a resin-scented arch.

As my sturdy vehicle bumped and juddered along, a white trail of dust was left behind sealing from view the world that I was so happily exchanging for the untouched paradise of nature that lay ahead. The pine scent increased, but every bumpy, tortuous mile was monotonously identical with the previous one.

At mile twenty-four where a tiny river had flooded over the road, I stopped to freshen up the water in the fish can and check the lashings of the canoe, and I was about to continue my journey when I remembered that there had been no rain for weeks. What could have caused the flood? It was the work of beavers which had dammed up the little river to make a deep water refuge, that had caused the roadside flood. There was no sign of life on the pool for it was middle afternoon, the forest was sleeping. To a person like me the silence of the backwoods brought a sense of deep relief to nerves slightly strained during the hectic drive. Then I remembered Camp Musquash and the distance still to travel. I started up the jeep and returned to the battle of keeping it moving along the grim surface of the track.

At the end of mile forty-six, I spotted the turning to the right which the map sheet told me was the road to Musquash. It was a pleasure to leave the dusty road at last and turn on to the long deserted route to the camp of which I had so often dreamed. The way led steadily down by tortuous bends, until it swung round an open spur of the mountain, and far below me I could see the deep and twisting glen of the great Missimi River. I pulled up, jumped out and reached for my binoculars, and gazed over the dark green hills of pine, larch, spruce and fir that rose and fell for fifty miles in all directions, eastwards to the Gulf, northward towards the province of Quebec, and westward to the State of Maine. It was a spectacle of the wealth and grandeur of eastern Canada, a sight that few Canadians have seen. As I stood there on that open spur of hill beside the overheated truck with its load of gear, I felt in some way a modern counterpart of the pioneering backwoodsmen of earlier days.

The spectacle of that wonderful view and the importance of the task ahead aroused a great excitement within me. A thousand feet below, the river meandered along a deep trench formed by the hills that interlaced one beyond the other, eastwards towards the Gulf of St Lawrence. The singing of its rushing waters came up in waves of sound from the white blurs of cataracts and waterfalls that separated tranquil stretches of the river. I followed its course through binoculars until I spotted Camp Musquash peeping shyly from a clearing in the young green conifers. It was a tiny group of ancient timber shacks, now all that remained of the long deserted lumber camp.

I jumped back into the truck and drove down in the tracks of the construction vehicles until I came to level ground and stopped before the rough log cabin that was to be my home. Over the entrance, a bleached skull of a giant moose, complete with horns, had been nailed. I unlocked the door and went inside to a room some twenty feet in length built from pine logs in the old traditional style. Two double-decker bedsteads stood at the far end, cupboards and boxes were stocked with tinned provisions, the cost of which would be deducted from my salary when the job was over. I grabbed a can of apple juice, opened it and quenched my thirst, I was hungry too but food could wait. I rushed out and found a smaller shed fitted with a huge glass window, and before it, on a table, stood a microscope, cases of instruments, bottles of killing liquid and cabinets of laboratory equipment. I explored the stables with their mangers and stalls. I sniffed the ancient musty smell of the time when horses toiled at the lumber in its previous occupation. The regenerated forest trees had grown again and stood silent in the heat of the evening, perhaps watching the strange visitor from another world who had come to live among them. Then I walked down to my beloved Missimi where the wooden counting fence was built at a shallow place across the river. I mounted the cat-walk and went along it to inspect the two square cages where the salmon and smolts would trap themselves on moving up or down the river when the gates were shut.

I stood on the wooden causeway in midstream and looked along the beautiful valley. Rising trout ringed the clear water as hatching insects surfaced, bird song rang far and wide across the forest, an osprey circled at a great height, and a white-tailed hind with a pair of tiny fawns on either side of her came daintily out of the undergrowth and stepped to the river's edge to drink. I stood on the cat-walk, frozen into immobility, conscious of every sound and movement on the water, the land, and in the air.

Both cages had been purposely left incomplete by the builders, so that during the period before my arrival when there was no one in attendance, the river was left open for the passage of salmon in both directions. My first job was to finish the cages and close the exit gates.

When I sunk the aquarium containing my twelve young fish in the river, a gauze lid permitted a constant flow of fresh water to pass through and keep them in good condition.

To find myself in such a river paradise after a year of intensive study, was difficult to believe. In the first glow of that great experience I realised that there was no one in the whole, wide world with whom I would have changed places on that warm summer evening. I walked back to the cabin and explored more carefully the cooking arrangements which now took precedence over everything else. A cylinder of gas was already connected to the stove, and presently the scent and sound of frying bacon filled the room. Camp Musquash was once again a home. I ate a great deal before I was satisfied and was soon exploring all over again. Most of the original buildings had been removed, and only the stables, laboratory, garage and a little hut which housed the gasoline engine that worked the generator had been left outside the main cabin. Thirty years must have passed since its previous occupation when the slopes echoed to the crash of axes and the yells of 'timber.' Fresh stands of larch and spruce had grown again, but here and there a giant white pine which had been spared, towered far above the younger trees. Sentinels from an older age perhaps, that could recall the days of the Mic Mac Indians and the French and British pioneers.

Satisfied at last, I came to a stop and sat down on the rough steps at the front door which commanded a view both up and down the valley. Before me the river cascaded over the rocks in a never-ending surge of sound that was music to the ears. A short distance above the falls, the freshly sawn timber that formed the framework of the counting fence stood above its clear reflection in the water, and beyond it, the great orange ball of the setting sun was tipping the saw-toothed edge of the forest skyline. Bird song had ceased, and only the occasional harsh scream of night hawks rang out sharply as they quartered the sky above the trees, and dived with fantastic speed to feed on the moths as they left the shelter of the branches. As each bird swooped and caught its moth, there came a rushing roar as the wing pinions broke the dive before the bird threw up into the sky again. This was my world, and I sat there lost in happy contemplation until a flash of silver caught my eye in the fast gathering dusk. It was the first salmon of the night's procession to leap the waterfall, to cleave the spillway above it. I remembered that I had not yet sealed the cage and closed the door which stopped the salmon on their upstream journey, and I ran to the fence and out along the cat-walk to the chamber, and trod down into the twelve inches of river water on the cage floor to lower the wall of bars and close the escape door thus sealing off the upper river from the running salmon. Then I climbed back on to the cage roof and lay down to await the arrival of the first fish. Very soon I saw the grey shape of a salmon in the clear water, moving quietly towards the fence. I saw it more clearly as it reached the close set mesh of bars that stood diagonally across the river, and it lay for several minutes under the shelter of the trestles before another salmon joined it. The first fish seemed to gather confidence from the arrival of the second, and both started nosing against the bars. The angular siting of the fence had been so planned that the impulse to swim against the current took the two fish ever nearer to the mouth of the cage.

I lay above them watching, and hardly moving my eyes as they approached the inviting flow of water that gurgled through the opening. Then silently the two grey shapes slid one behind the other into the darkness of their night's captivity.

I had witnessed the working of the trap, so I stood up and walked back to the cabin, wondering what the morning's catch would reveal. I started up the generator, switched on the lights, plugged in the wireless and listened to the music of the outside world. Before turning in for the night, I wrote up my diary, then picked up the telephone and gave my home number. My people were awaiting the call. It was strange to speak to them from the deep seclusion of the forest, and that was my last conscious thought as I lay in bed that night, exhausted but supremely happy.

THREE

INTERNATIONAL POACHING

As the first grey light of early dawn grew clearer in the eastern sky, I woke. It was too early for the dawn chorus, but already I had work to do. Pulling on trousers and sweater, I grabbed a torch and went out into the cool gloaming of the scented daybreak. Even with the prospect of my first inspection of the counting fence at hand, I was momentarily spell-bound by the infinite peace and wonder of the river and the forest as it passed through that short period of transcendental beauty of half-light between the death of night and the birth of day.

Across the glen, the silhouette of the trees stood darkly against a backcloth of fading stars and the last traces of the aurora borealis. The river murmured over the rocks as it swept downstream, faint whisps of mist rose off the water, and the night scent of the river and the forest blended into a fragrance that only he who sees his river before the dawn, can know.

I walked slowly at first through the tall wet grass at the river's edge, enjoying the scent and sound of those magic moments before sunrise. On reaching the counting fence I mounted the ramp and moved along the cat-walk until I came to the cage roof and lay down on the sodden timbers, to look inside to see what the ocean had sent.

It was not fully light and the cage floor appeared dark in the light of the torch. It was a little time before I realised that the water that covered the floor of the cage was black with salmon. It was still too dark to begin work on the fish, and I returned to the cabin to await full light. While the coffee approached the boil I prepared for the task of marking the catch. Into a glass-bottomed bucket I placed a box of numbered plastic tags mounted on stainless steel wire, pliers and tweezers. Then I pulled on a pair of rubber fishing-waders, and drank my coffee. By the time I left the cabin, the early sunlight had reached the crest of the opposite hill, and as I retraced my steps through the riverine grass, the rattle of a woodpecker rang down from the spruce trees, the birds had started to sing. Whisky jacks flitted to and fro and the music of gay Scottish folk tunes followed me from the radio which I had forgotten to switch off.

I crouched on the cage roof again and looked down at the shoal of captive salmon as they lay side by side in the gentle gurgling turbulence of the water. For some minutes I was too excited to open the trap-door to descend among the fish. The careful, record-keeping scientist in me was temporarily banished in face of this moving revelation of fish migration. I lay for at least five minutes in the sunlight of that never to be forgotten dawn, staring down at the blue black wanderers from the sea.

Like their predecessors of the autumn, they lay in the shade of the cage, meekly accepting their enforced respite after a river journey of well over a hundred miles against the current. It was July and the fish felt no desperate urge to reach good spawning water, for the embryonic spawn was dormant within them. Where had they been in their ocean wandering? What sights had those strange unwinking eyes beheld? I pondered on the fantastic sequence of adventure and escape they had all passed through in order to live long enough to reach their splendid shape and size. As the light increased, I was able to recognise the different shades of colour which varied from the light brown backs of some that closely resembled the colour of stones, to deeper, darker shades of turquoise bluish black. The light brown fish were salmon which had taken longer to come up from the sea, while the dark blues had come up quickly and caught up the slow ones at the counting fence. The camouflaging influence of new surroundings had not yet changed the pigment in their skins from the deeper blue of the ocean which they had so recently left. The dark blue-blacks and lighter browns lay side by side, the dorsal fins and tail tops of the bigger ones breaking the surface. As the sunlight reached them in the pen the colour differences became more obvious. The brown fish merged into the background, and I saw the spotted flanks that never fail to bring a thrill to the minds of anglers. I unlocked the door, climbed down into the cage, and started my first morning's work.

My chief concern was to avoid panicking the salmon and I moved with extreme slowness until I was actually crouching among them. I remained in this position for some time, looking closely at the black spotted silver of their flanks. In some strange way, I felt a kinship with them all, for the great Missimi River which I loved was also their river. For them no other river in the world would do, they had grown from spawn in Missimi gravel, then swum far into the Atlantic and returned, and only in this same gravel would they be content to plant their own spawn when the time should come.

I selected my first fish, and very quietly placed my right hand over its head thus sealing off its eyes to prevent it seeing me. Then I grasped it by the tail with the left hand and guided it into a long wooden strait-jacket where it could not struggle. The head was hidden in the covered end, and my right hand was free to insert the hollow needle through the skin of its back in front of the dorsal fin. Then I inserted the wire of a numbered tag into the hollow needle and withdrew it, leaving the wire in the skin, the two ends were twisted together with the pliers, and the first migrant salmon of the Missimi plan was marked for life. I moved the strait-jacket to the door, where the fish regained the freedom of the river.

Thus my first salmon was numbered and released, and as it disappeared upstream I felt the romantic naturalist within me change to the role of scientific investigator. There was a contribution to make in solving the salmon's secret, there was a job to do. I covered the head of the next fish within reach, seized its tail with the other hand, guided it into the strait-jacket, fixed the tag and allowed it to follow the first one into the freedom of the river. The process was repeated again and again, as the morning sun climbed higher into the sky. Occasionally I removed a scale from the flank of a fish, with the help of the tweezers, and put it into a little envelope for examination under the microscope, the length of these fish was noted on the envelope, together with tag numbers. Gradually the fish were marked until at last the pen was empty.

Then I turned to the other cage in which the downstream swimming little salmon smolts collected as they dropped back on their first migration to the sea. Like the adults they too moved only at night, but by July they had all gone down and the run was over except for a dozen little smolts which were clustered in a corner of the cage; although only six inches in length, they were already three years old and the time had come when for them the river had served its purpose, the urge to move downstream had started, and under cover of darkness they dropped quietly back towards the great unknown.

I stepped into the cage and netted the little fish one at a time, and holding them in a specially made rubber holding block, pierced the skin of the back and attached a numbered tag in the same way as I had for the adults. The delicate smolt in this transition period of adolescence was at a critical stage and it was a difficult task as the silvery scales were so easily rubbed off.

One after another I marked the smolts and turned them out of the cage to hide in the current until darkness would break their reluctance to stay still with heads upstream, and they would turn away and move on towards the sea.

In recent years records have shown that from every twenty-five smolts marked on this downstream migration, so great is the loss from predators, that an average of only one adult salmon is recovered as it returns upstream to spawn.

For me, those early days at the counting fence were the most rewarding I have ever spent in my life. At dawn I would mark and release the nights' catch, and as I did so, crouching in the water, hidden behind the bars of

Fish hatchery men removing salmon from the holding pond for egg stripping. (*Department of Fisheries of Canada*)

A cock and hen salmon on the spawning bed, showing the mottling and enlarged jaw and kype of the male fish at mating time. (From the author's film *Kingdom*

the cage, I was invisible to the forest dwellers. A cavalcade of wild creatures was always in evidence along the river as night gave way to each new day. Bears, deer, and the giant moose came to drink and feed, beavers, musk rats, racoons, foxes and otters put in regular appearances. From this hide in midstream, my chance of observing nature was unique. Only one thing disturbed the peaceful idyll of my existence, it was the faint note of a distant aircraft that seemed to fly only in the very early mornings.

One morning, on walking towards the fence, I saw a long winged bird circling above the cage. Then even as I recognised it as an osprey or giant fish hawk, it swung away over the tree tops.

The run of big salmon had been slowly tailing off for several days, and four-year-old grilse salmon weighing between two and four pounds were coming up from the sea. I tagged each one in the same way as the older fish, and wondered why they came, as they were all too young to spawn.

On the morning when the osprey was seen over the cage, I marked many grilse as usual. The first fish, a three-pounder, was quickly marked and released, then a second was netted, and brought towards the strait-jacket. As I did so the sound of rushing air made me look up-river in time to see the osprey (which had watched the grilse leave the trap) at the end of its amazing dive. It entered the water talons first, to disappear with a great splash, its long wings stretching upright over its back. A moment later it surfaced, its hooked beak and eagle eyes looking strangely out of place on the surface of the water. Then it thrashed with its mighty wings and rose skywards bearing the grilse in its talons. I watched it rise by easy spirals, high into the dawn sky, then it went into a long glide towards the north until it disappeared beyond the hills, in the direction of the family of young ospreys which would soon be breakfasting off fresh run salmon. Life was so short that I thought of the continual effort of feeding my captive parr in the midst of that natural sanctuary. The search for suitable insect food to satisfy their ravenous appetites had palled, and that day I released them to take their chance in the river.

Some days after the osprey incident, the sound of a vehicle coming down the long hill brought me out of the laboratory. It was Bill Machett the gatekeeper.

'How d'ye?' came his cheery greeting as he brought his truck to a standstill in a cloud of dust. 'Had to go up to Halford's, so thought I'd drop by and see how you're makin' out 'ere.'

'I'm doing fine, thanks,' I replied. 'Come in the cabin and have a drink. I don't get crowded out with callers every day up here.'

He climbed out of his truck, beat some of the dust off his jacket, and sat down. I poured him a drink.

'Aye, you've only had that guy from the Anglers' Association, and then that party of scientists from the Fisheries Research place who've come up to see you since you've been 'ere?'

'Yes, that's all,' I agreed.

'I guess you won't be pestered much with visitors up here, it's an ideal spot for your job,' Machett continued, 'but I'm surprised the river wardens ain't been up yet. Still, the less you see of them the better, but they'll be around sooner or later, and when they come, there's usually a bit of trouble afoot. No, I guess nobody'll be pesterin' ye up here, but it's funny that none of those guys from Halford's lush fishing camp ain't got around to callin' on ye yet.'

'Who are they—anglers?' I asked.

'I mean those newspaper millionaire guys, the big customers who buy pulp from Halford's for making paper. They gets invited to the Missimi Club for a week's fishing. Everything's laid on pretty lush I can tell ye. Eight guests at a time, there's two guides to each guest. The club's about twenty miles downstream from here on the opposite bank, there's several fishing camps there, they all belong to Halford's. The road only goes to one camp and you can only get to the others by power-driven canoe; it's the finest fishing and probably the most exclusive club in the world. You ought to try and get down there some time.'

'I can't see that coming off,' I told him. 'Anyway, I've got plenty to do here, though the big run's tailing off a bit now, and if the water goes down much lower, I guess they'll stop running altogether till we get a drop of fresh.'

'Yes, we want rain pretty bad,' he agreed.

We yarned on for some time before I took him out to look over the counting fence in which he showed the greatest interest. But I could not stop thinking of the fabulous fishing camp to which millionaires were invited from distant parts of the world to come and fish for salmon in my river. It was not generally known even to the village folk who lived along the highway, that parties of the world's most influential press magnates were invited to the scented heart of the Missimi forest for a week's relaxation. I pressed Bill Machett for more details of the fishing camp until my curiosity was satisfied, and

Bill took his leave. Some days after Machett's visit I heard another vehicle descending the track from the lumber road, and went to investigate. A Land Rover pulled up and I noticed the miniature searchlight mounted over the cab. Two men got out, dressed in the familiar green uniform of Fishery Protection Wardens.

'Guess this is Camp Musquash?' said the first, introducing himself as Superintendent Baxter. 'This is my assistant Charlie Donovan,' he said, turning to his driver. 'You're Wayne Douglas?' he asked, as they moved into the hut and relaxed over cans of beer. We were soon good friends, although they had not said why they had visited me.

'How's the counting fence working out?' asked the Superintendent. 'We'd like to have a look at it when we've cooled off a bit.'

I assumed that as they were officials from the government department that catered for the protection of salmon and supervised the angling interests, their concern was normal: they were the policemen of the river, and I felt obliged to regard their visit—although they had not said so—as a form of inspection both of the fence and my work.

I produced my record book, and showed them the daily inventory of all salmon handled and marked. They examined it in detail and were visibly impressed by the numbers set down after each night's passage.

'Well now we know exactly what's happening in this river, for the first time ever I guess,' said one of the men with obvious satisfaction.

I could not help feeling a glow of pleasure at the remark, for this was the first sign of recognition from an outside source.

'This is only the start,' I told them, 'it may take a long time yet, but we'll succeed in the end, after building up a mass of evidence year by year, to present a true picture of the salmon's life in fresh water and perhaps in the sea as well.'

The two men glanced at each other with the look that experts have when a sweeping statement is made by a younger man.

'Well let's go and see your lay-out,' said the senior man. They got up and walked along the well-worn pathway to the fence. I unlocked the door and the wardens peered into the empty cage through which a current, barely eight inches deep, passed quietly over the wooden floor.

They pressed me for all details on my approach to the job, how the fish were handled, marked and released, to what extent they were marked or bruised by nets and other means. To everything I had an answer, and they appeared to be satisfied.

On returning to the hut, they settled down once more while I prepared a meal. Then I gradually sensed that the two men were interested in something which lay outside the fence and the research work, and it puzzled me.

'Is there anything else you'd like to see?' I asked them after we had eaten.

'No, that's all right Douglas,' replied the superintendent, 'you seem to be doing a good job, the pity is that most of those fish that you've marked have probably been eaten down in the Boston district of the U.S.A. by now.'

I failed to see any humour in the joke. To me salmon were not a subject for that sort of humour, and I paid little heed, but waited until the milk boiled.

'Here it is, gentlemen,' I said, 'I hope you enjoyed your meal.'

'What we jest said didn't seem to worry you Douglas,' the warden commented as they took their steaming cups.

'I suppose you're entitled to your little joke,' I replied sourly.

'It's no joking matter Douglas, bring out your book again.'

I brought down the book from its shelf and it was consulted once more, and then to my utter amazement, the superintendent produced a plastic tag. The number marked on it corresponded to a tag number which I had fixed to a salmon in the early part of the month.

The blank dismay on my face prompted the superintendent to begin his story.

'I guess you'd like to know how I came by this tag,' he began.

'Well some guy down in Boston was passing a fish shop and he saw six salmon laid out on the slab, he must have been a bit of an angler I guess, 'cause he went up to have a good look at them, and noticed that the skin in front of the dorsal fin on each fish had been punctured. He got curious and asked the merchant about it, and was told that one fish had had a metal marking plate which he cut off. This guy asked if it could be found. It was lucky they'd only just been done, and the tag was produced and given to this Boston chap. Now he must have read that the Canadian Government was offering a dollar apiece reward for returned tags and he sent it straight off to the Fisheries Research Board office. They had a record of all tag numbers supplied to you, and as you're the only one tagging so far, they assumed that the fish that carried this tag must have passed through your hands up here on the Missimi. Fishery Research Department has turned it over to us to investigate. We've got through to R.C.M.P. at Ottawa, they've contacted the Boston police, and every fish shop in Boston is now being watched for salmon with your pin pricks on the skin of its back.'

I stared down at the tell-tale tag and its bent bit of wire, with all the incredulousness of a murderer faced with the recovered murder weapon. I was at first too stupefied to speak, but when I found my voice I said, 'Boston, why that's six hundred miles from here, how could they get them there?'

After a short but icy silence, the superintendent bent forward and with a penetrating stare at me, asked coolly, 'How could *who* get them there? We have a pretty good idea how they got to Boston, all we want to know is who got them, and how they caught them, and we thought perhaps you may be able to help.'

Slowly I realised the position in which I was placed. For nearly a month I had been alone at the camp in the middle of the wilds, during which time almost seven thousand dollars worth of salmon had passed through my hands.

I had been entrusted with the job by a body of scientists whose thoughts, like my own, never contemplated killing and marketing the fish. But six had been exhibited for sale in a city six hundred miles away in the States. There was no mistaking the thoughts in the minds of the two men who watched me so intently. They were not scientists, they were professional detectives of the river, men whose lives had been devoted to enforcing the fishery laws, and combating all methods of poaching. I was the central figure in the whole unsavoury business.

'This is the position, Mr Douglas,' continued the superintendent. 'We suspect that great numbers of Missimi salmon are being caught by a gang of poachers somewhere in this forest and somehow smuggled over the border into the States. Now we've gone very thoroughly into your background, many questions have been asked about you and we've come to the conclusion that you're not the sort of guy to have any part of this poaching racket. We're convinced that it's going on in a big way. Now put your thinking cap on and try and recollect anything that's seemed suspicious since you got here.'

'Had any visitors, Mr Douglas?' asked the junior warden.

I told them of the visit by the research people, the Anglers' Association man, and Bill Machett the gatekeeper, all of whom were obviously above suspicion.

'No trucks passing on the Halford Road?' continued the warden.

I thought hard, and was about to admit that nothing had aroused my suspicions, when I suddenly remembered the aircraft noise. 'There's been some strange movements of an aircraft when I come to think back a bit,' I said. 'It wasn't one of the big ones, I'm sure, and its engine seems to die away suddenly, then I hear it again perhaps a day or two later. I've heard it several times, but I put it down to something to do with the lumber camp, though it's not in that direction at all.'

The announcement about the aircraft created an immediate impression on the two men, although they said nothing until I finished.

'What direction d' you hear it in?' asked the superintendent.

'Well it always comes from the same direction I guess, somewhere about North-West by West, straight up the valley,' I said.

They produced a detailed survey map of the area and orientated it on the table.

'Now,' continued the superintendent, 'here's the camp, and we run a line up the valley slightly west of North-West. How far away would you say the noise is when it stops?'

'About two to three miles,' I replied. 'Somewhere about where that lake is,' and I pointed to where the river widened out considerably to form a long narrow lake.

'Ever been up there?' asked the warden.

'No, it's impossible, the bush is too thick,' I told them.

'What about your canoe,' asked the warden.

'That's impossible too. I tried it once, there's a series of rapids between rocks and portage is too difficult beyond a point half-way to the lake.'

'Well now Mr Douglas, you've helped us a lot by mentioning the plane, that confirms our theories at Headquarters. These Yankee poachers are coming in from the State of Maine, very high over the border in the early hours of the morning and dropping down to the source of the Missimi, following it along to this lake and landing on it with the help of floats, then catching their salmon—probably netting them—and flying back to the States next morning. This may have been going on for a long time, and we might never have spotted it but for your little tag and that lynx-eyed Boston guy.'

I asked if there was anything I could do to help.

'I've got to be off back now,' the chief warden replied, 'but I'm leaving Charlie here with you until you hear that plane again, permission's been O.K.d by the

Research Board. I'd like you to keep a twenty-four hour listening watch between you, and next time you hear it, ring my office or home immediately—depending on whether it's in the day or night.' With that he got up, and we went outside. Baxter restarted the truck and drove away up the hill, and we watched him disappear in a cloud of dust.

We sat on the porch steps discussing the situation in detail for some time and the more I thought about it the more dejected I became.

'After all the money spent on this project, to think that those hoodlums should come up here and mess the whole thing up like this by taking my marked fish out of the river to sell down in the States, it's too bad!'

'If there ever was an understatement that's about it,' said the warden. 'Don't you realise this is a complicated international poaching incident, probably done on a very big scale. The moment we hear that airplane come back and stop, we report it to the chief, then I guess he'll have the fishery plane ready with a boarding party and they'll be coming up here to nab them. It's my guess that they're netting the fish from dinghies. Tomorrow morning we'll set off at first light in your canoe, get upstream as far as we can, then beach her, and cut our way through the bush until we come to the lake, the netting's probably done at that point. I want to get evidence and let the chief know, it'll help him when he comes to make his swoop.'

'O.K.,' I said. 'I'll keep the fence gates shut to stop the salmon getting through until this job is cleared up.'

'No,' replied the warden emphatically. 'Let the fish go on up unmarked for a day or so, these guys have got to be caught with a good haul of evidence. If we can present a strong case, we'll get the aircraft confiscated, that should check any others from trying. When this story gets into the press it'll make headlines and unless there's a cracking fine the other gangs may fancy their chances. If we can get the plane confiscated everything will be O.K.'

That night the trap-door was lifted, and the river left free for the passage of salmon.

On the following morning at first light, I got the canoe ready and we paddled steadily against the current. After about a mile, the turbulence where it poured out of a gorge, prevented any further progress. We hid the canoe in the undergrowth, and completed the rest of the journey on foot. The river level had dropped considerably and there were places where progress on foot was easy between the low summer level and the ice marks of spring. At other places we were obliged to climb through the dense forest, and everywhere the tangled undergrowth lay over a carpet of rotten tree trunks and the going was slow in the growing heat of the morning.

At last we regained the river beyond the gorge where we could move more easily. Far ahead the Missimi could be seen gradually widening out into a lake. The warden took out his binoculars and surveyed the water.

'Yes,' he said suddenly. 'I thought as much, I can see the line of floats that holds the net across the river. We've struck it son!'

I borrowed his glasses and saw in the distance a row of dots stretching over the surface of the river.

'Come on,' I urged. 'We'll soon pull that away to let the fish through.'

'Not quite so fast,' replied the warden. 'That's about the last thing we're gonna do, I guess. They'll be along again shortly and we mustn't let 'em know that we are on to them. That's it for sure, for all we know there may be a gang camping out there catching fish every night and the plane just comes to pick up the haul. I guess we'd better be dead careful from here on; if there's anyone there, and they spot us, our plan'll be upset. You'd best sit tight, and I'll go on alone and take a closer look. For God's sake don't show yourself while I'm gone.'

Charlie Donovan left me sitting at the edge of the forest while he moved forward with ever-increasing caution. He climbed higher along the sloping hill until he judged that he was above the net. He descended with still greater caution until the faint scent from a log fire reached him, and he stopped to listen. He recognised the drawl of an American accent and although he failed to catch the words, it told him all he wished to know. He longed to know how many men were there, but he dared not risk discovery and moved back in silence to the point where I was waiting.

'They're there all right,' he said as he rejoined me. 'Must be two at least, probably three. We must get back to your place and ring through to the boss.'

We reached the canoe and paddled down to Camp Musquash in the heat of the afternoon. Charlie Donovan rang up the superintendent and told him of the discovery.

'That's good work Donovan,' came the reply. 'Don't go near again, but keep listening and the moment you hear the plane, give me that call. I've been on to Halifax and they've dispatched an amphibian and boarding party. I'm awaiting them now, so keep listening and we'll have 'em in the bag.'

That night we took turns in a two-hourly listening watch outside the cabin, and about four o'clock, as the light over the north-eastern horizon was growing brighter, I began to hear the far away hum of an engine coming from the west. The plane seemed to be flying low and the purring sound had none of the power drone of the airline passenger planes. I rushed into the hut, shook Donovan and we went outside to listen, and in the calm of the morning, we heard again the gentle drone beyond the tree-tops.

'He's keeping low to muffle his sound, though I don't know why he should bother in this great loneliness,' said Charlie.

Then the sound of the engine began to die away, and some seconds later it stopped quite suddenly.

Then followed a good-natured scramble between the two of us to be first to grab the phone and give the superintendent's home number. I listened to the conversation with a beating heart.

'Baxter speaking,' came the reply.

'This is Donovan, sir. The kite's just arrived, her engines have just stopped, so what's the next move?'

'O.K.' came the voice at the other end. 'I've got everything ready here, we'll get cracking as soon as I can wake up the boys. I want you two on the scene as well, so get back to the lake as quick as you can. If you get there before us don't show yourselves. I'm sending a car load of mounties to Camp Musquash to get up-river on foot. Your poachers may scatter when they see us, so tell Douglas to immobilise his truck.'

'Good luck, sir,' replied the warden, but his chief had already rung off.

We had a quick breakfast, then packed some food and set off by canoe along the dawn-lit splendour of the river. We left the canoe at the same point as on the previous day and followed our tracks through the forest until we came as close to the camp as we dared, and sat down to await the patrol plane.

Below us we could hear the sound of voices on the river, the excited voices of men catching salmon in all the freedom and abandon of poachers who believed the nearest human beings were over fifty miles away. We both longed to see what was going on.

'Can't we climb one of these trees and have a look over?' I whispered.

'No,' hissed the warden, 'they'd spot it swaying straight away, we've got to be ready to close in as soon as Baxter arrives to distract their attention. We start moving down as soon as we hear the plane.

The tension of the wait was released by the yells of a pair of great northern divers on the far side of the lake who voiced their displeasure at the invasion of their privacy, in a cacophony of sub-human screams that echoed about the wooded hills.

'The loons don't like the Yanks by the sound of it,' whispered Charlie, and I agreed with him. The mad laughter of the divers is one of the most strangely stirring sounds in the world of nature.

'As soon as the plane shows up I guess these characters'll scram into the forest if they can,' said Charlie, 'and that's where we come in, we've got to stop 'em. Ever done this sort of thing before?'

'Never,' I grunted and I didn't tell him that my heart was beating wildly with the excitement of it.

'Well just think of your salmon, and the damage done

to your work, that should spur you on. But we'll not have any trouble with 'em I reckon.

We crept slowly down the slope until only a hundred yards separated us from the little camp where the narrow lake opened between the rift in the hills.

'Far enough,' whispered my companion after studying the situation. 'When we make our entry you go to the right and I'll take the left, act very cool and dignified, put on a good show of confidence, and they'll collapse like frightened rabbits.'

Then we heard the far off drone of an approaching aircraft.

'That's probably Baxter,' whispered Charlie. 'I hope they cut round the hills and approach from the far end and stop here, because the Yankee plane is probably this end.'

The sound of the engines grew fainter as it moved away to the west, it was obviously very low and moving round. We waited breathlessly for several minutes for our first view of the plane, then it swung into sight at the top end of the lake and roared lower and lower as it raced on until its floats were hissing over the water.

'Come on Wayne boy,' Donovan said, and we rushed down to the camp and out on to the grass beside the river in the traditional style of water bailiffs.

The American plane was tied up near the bank and four men were in the act of transferring boxes of salmon to it. They stood paralysed with fear as they watched our fishery patrol plane roaring towards them. Then suddenly they seemed to regain enough courage to turn and run for the safety of the forest. Donovan and I barred their route.

'O.K. you guys, I guess your game's up,' Donovan

shouted. At sight of us they stopped, rooted to their tracks in the long grass, while the fishery plane roared up to the edge of the lake where three wardens and two mounties jumped out and waded ashore.

'Good work boys,' greeted the superintendent as he came up. 'I thought I'd give you time to get up here first and stop these guys if they tried to make a break into the timber. Not that they'd have got out of these woods alive,' he added turning to the four frightened men, 'so if there's any more of yer, give 'em a shout or they'll never be seen agen I reckon.'

Then he turned to one of the mounties. 'Better immobilise their kite in case one of them makes a break in it while we're packing up.'

The illegally taken fish had been stowed away between ice in boxes of four. We counted fifty-five salmon, and I noticed that every fish bore my puncture mark but the tags had been removed. The net was taken out of the river, the dinghies deflated, the camp broken up, and all the evidence stowed away in the two planes. We forced the poachers to do most of the work. One of the mounties took charge of the American plane, the wardens, the prisoners, the netting gear and the salmon were equally distributed in the two aircraft. Then they taxied out into the lake and roared away over the woodlands.

Charlie and I were left at the water's edge to wave farewell before turning away for camp. As we entered the dense bush again I turned for a last look at the lake. Missimi Lake Game Reserve lay blue and shining in the afternoon sun, once more the undisputed haunt of its rightful occupants, and restored to its silent and lonely splendour.

FOUR

JOURNEY BY CANOE

After I had all but forgotten the excitement of the Missimi lake adventure I had another visitor. I was in the laboratory at the time classifying salmon scales under the microscope, when a long, low Cadillac saloon came swaying and bucking down the rutted trail. It stopped in front of the lab. window and its enormous passenger disengaged himself with the chauffeur's assistance. He looked a somewhat over-dressed fisherman, clad in a brand-new angler's outfit which sat uneasily on his ample frame.

He was obviously one of the guests from Halford's camp, I had been warned of a possible visit from that quarter and it was suggested—in a subtle way—that I should handle such visitors with tact.

The great pulp company had taken advantage of the natural facilities of the river for entertaining its customers on a salmon fishing holiday under unrivalled conditions. The Missimi Club had been formed for this purpose and had grown into a fabulous fishing camp. Throughout the season, relays of tycoons from both sides of the Atlantic, most of whom purchased pulp from Halford's mill, were entertained under conditions of extreme luxury.

I came out of the laboratory to give my customary greeting to visitors, but the American beat me to it.

'You the guy that lives all alone up here? Kinda Robinson Crusoe existence I guess. Is that a microscope you've got in there? What's cookin'?' He spoke like a machine gun.

'Oh, I've just been taking scale readings,' I said, treating my visitor to the compliment of assuming that he knew what I meant by scale reading.

'What's that?' he snapped.

'Well, I keep a record of the ages of some of the salmon that pass up-river,' I replied.

'And how in Heaven's name d'you set about telling the age of a salmon?' he asked.

'By counting the number of summers and winters recorded on its scales,' I said.

The blank look that settled over his face indicated that he thought I was taking him for a ride. It had probably been many years since one of my age had dared such a thing. 'I'm Harry B. Goldup,' he said, 'what's your name?' I told him quickly and before he could tell me that he'd report me for insolence I invited him into the laboratory and asked him to look through the lens. A salmon scale was already in focus, and for the first time Goldup saw the wonderful revelation of nature by which the salmon's age can be accurately told. He stared down at the mass of concentric rings that covered the surface of the scale, resembling in some way the annual rings of a sawn-off tree trunk. His large fleshy fingers which doubtless had written out many six figure cheques, adjusted the knobs for better focusing. He was amazed by what he saw, but still needed help to interpret the meaning behind the arrangement of the rings.

'About one ring is formed every month or so of the

salmon's life,' I explained, 'and as spring turns to summer and food gets more plentiful, growth speeds up, so during each summer you see the rings spaced wider apart. In winter when food is scarce growth slows down, and the rings come closer together.' I paused to let my words sink in, and all the while Goldup's eye never left the lens. I continued, 'Now sir, you should be able to count the widely spaced groups of rings and tell me how many summers that fish has spent in the sea.'

The American looked up from the lens and I could see the dawning of this new knowledge spreading over his face.

'Well,' he exploded, 'I do believe you've got something here. As far as I can see that salmon was only four years old.'

'Quite right as far as the sea is concerned,' I told him. 'But you must add three years of river life shown by the concentration of small rings in the middle, before the salmon entered the sea. That fish hatched out seven years ago, sir.'

He returned to the microscope as one for whom a mystery had been revealed but who was as yet unable to grasp it.

'You mean to tell me that this passing of time is printed on every scale on the salmon's body?'

'That's right,' I said. 'The hardships of each winter show up on every scale. It's nature's writing for the benefit of those who can read. It's the same when a young bird of prey goes through a period of hunger while its feathers are growing, the hunger trace can be seen across the wing feathers. It's the same with these scales I guess.'

Harry B. Goldup capitulated absolutely, and his

enthusiastic pleasure at his discovery was rewarding to see. Then, excited by his new-found knowledge, he rushed outside to where the camp truck (which had been following his car) had arrived with it's canoe slung on a trailer. Three guides climbed stiffly out of the cab but were given little time to recover. Goldup bawled at them. 'Do any of you guys know how to tell the age of salmon?'

His guides were tough Canadians whose lives had been spent in the service of anglers. They had travelled the Missimi by canoe summer after summer and their livelihood was bound up with the fishing guests at the Camp and the movement of the salmon.

Clad in fish-stained lumber jackets and hunting caps they came up to the steps of the lab. and one at a time gave their theories for telling a salmon's age, to all of which Goldup, in his brand-new fishing outfit, cried a triumphant 'No!' I found it all great fun to watch.

'D'you see this youngster,' he said, turning to me. 'He knows!' Then talking directly to me, he said, 'You know what these guys have been trying to tell us down at the Camp? That there's a big salmon in the million dollar pool there that's supposed to be a hundred years old. That's the sort of nonsense they try to get us to swallow down there.

'This fish is supposed to weigh over sixty pounds. We've seen him all right and he's taken some flies off us, but no tackle will hold him I guess.'

Relationship between the millionaire visitors and the New Brunswick guides were on the friendliest terms. No trace of old world subservience is seen on the banks of Canadian salmon rivers; worldly values are obliterated, and hearty leg-pulling is carried out on both sides.

'Come in here you dumb clucks,' shouted Goldup gleefully. 'We'll show yuh how to tell. Go on boy, you tell 'em.'

I was reluctant at first to go through the details again as I expected the two guides with their vast practical experience would write me off as a 'line-shooter.' But Goldup made me repeat the explanation and I invited them to look through the lens. They showed only mild surprise and I could see that Goldup was annoyed. He failed to realise that these men lived by killing or helping to kill game; their interest in fish, animals, and birds lay in the pleasure of hunting them by rod, rifle, or trap. During the fall they hunted, during the winter they trapped, and during the spring and summer they acted as fishing guides at the Missimi Club. I had grown up among such men and was not surprised by their lack of interest at the revelations of a microscope. They were accustomed to be respected as experts by the men whom they guided on the river. Now, on this occasion I had stolen their thunder.

'What about that hundred-year-old salmon now,' scoffed Goldup at the guides, and turning to me he said, 'I'm sure gonna catch that fish before I break camp next week, and we'll get his exact age. What about coming down and bringing your microscope with you?'

'I'd like that,' I told him as, in his abrupt way, he turned to go. 'Come on now,' he commanded, 'let's get away down river, I want to see these famous rapids of yours.' The high pressure nervous energy which dominated his New York existence could not be changed, and for all his size he was obviously tireless.

The canoe was unstrapped from its trailer and carried to the river's edge below the falls, where the two guides helped him into a cushioned seat and laid his rod beside him. One guide stood in the bow with a long pole to punt away from rocks in the shallows, while his partner took his seat in the stern to control the outboard engine. In this way they moved off gently with the current over the clear shallow water. The driver climbed back into the truck and drove off in the dusty wake of the Cadillac. Then the outboard engine shattered the peace of the valley, and I watch the canoe's stem rise slowly as it gathered speed to skim away along the tree reflected waterway until it disappeared round a bend in the river and peace returned again to Camp Musquash.

Some days later the phone rang.

'Is that Mr Douglas? Camp Missimi here, manager speaking, Dan Maskell. Mr Goldup's been talking about your theory for telling a salmon's age.'

'It's not my theory,' I informed him, 'it's as old as the hills.'

'Never mind that,' said the manager, 'the guests here want to meet you and hear all about it. Can you come down tomorrow if I send the canoe for you?'

'Yes siree,' I replied. 'What time?'

'Let's see now,' said Maskell. 'I can spare the men right away if you could put 'em up for the night at your place, then you can start first thing in the morning. How's that?'

'Just fine,' I said with enthusiasm, and sat back to contemplate with relish the prospect of a twenty-five miles journey by canoe along the most beautiful stretches of the finest river in the world.

Later that same day the fishing camp truck again descended the hill with the canoe on tow which was soon removed from its trailer. Then the truck started back leaving the two guides as my guests for the night.

On the following morning only three small grilse were in the cage, I marked and released them and closed both gates. Throughout July no rain had fallen and the river level had gone so low that the big salmon had stopped travelling along the warm shallows even at night. The run of fish had come to a standstill along the whole length of the upper river. I felt that I had earned a little respite and knew that there would be nothing more to record until heavy rain brought a rise in the water when the salmon would move again.

Then the canoe was put on the river and we stepped in and drifted away over the clear shallows until the water was deep enough to start the outboard. The engine sprang to life and the graceful craft gathered speed in a long glide in which the stem rose high over the froth-decked surface, and for me the ride of a lifetime had begun.

Hundreds of swallows flittered, glided and dipped to the river's surface to drink and bathe on the wing. After the water impact they rose to shake their feathers and preen as they flew, then continued hawking for insects in the early shadows of the pines. Big red-breasted thrushes like giant robins fed on grassy patches as the dawn wind crept along the valley and set the aspens dancing.

The guides maintained a glum silence and I was so transported with the thrill of the fast glide over the water that conversation was superfluous.

One bend after another revealed the ever-changing beauty of the deep trench of the valley. As I watched the passing backcloth to the river, it seemed as though Nature herself had designed the valley's rugged inaccessibility as protection for the salmon's journey along that part of its route. The steep sides rose sharply from the river's edge where in places even a trail would be impossible to cut.

Tranquil reaches alternated with cascading rapids; movement was only possible by canoe in one direction.

We skimmed on at speed, and on either side, the riverine branches of the willows were bent and skinned of bark by the passage of spring ice, even large trees were barked and bent and broken. Leaves of saplings that grew above the ice line, had been eaten by deer, the browse line showed clearly to a height of five feet. In places the deer paths came down from the tangled wilderness of the hills to the willow and maple browsing pastures near the water. Sometimes we saw the crossing places of the deer where they still followed the age-old causeways of the ancient caribou migration trails.

Rounding a bend we came upon an enormous eagle standing on a rock in midstream. It rose, with sunlight flashing off the hard pinions of its wings and climbed easily into the sky, the snow-white tail and head still visible as it banked and circled majestically out of the valley.

A family of wild duck went skittering over the surface to disappear round a bend of the river ahead.

'Shelducks,' shouted one of the guides, for that was the local name given to the agile mergansers which we had just seen. I knew them for these rapacious fish-eating ducks that could move in the water like miniature torpedoes and took enormous toll of young salmon in Canadian rivers.

Very gradually I noticed that the speed of the canoe was increasing. The sides of the valley, which had been steep throughout the journey, now increased their pitch, the grandeur of the scenery grew wilder with every bend in the river. Gigantic boulders appeared, and all the while the deep-throated rumble of the first cataract of Hell's Gorge grew ever louder.

The guide in the bow stood up and held his steel shod pole ready for the rocks, and I waited with a thrill of anticipation for the battle that lay ahead. As the booming increased I could feel the cool mist of the spindrift that was blowing up the valley, and noticed that the grass and moss on the rocks was much greener than the parched grass further upstream. The distant rumble of the cataracts increased, and the valley sides became more rocky. Movement grew swifter, and then some distance ahead the river seemed suddenly to disappear. From our position almost at water level it looked as though we were heading for the top of a waterfall. The engine was stopped and taken inboard as we neared the edge, then we swung into the spillway where the tow took charge. There was a sudden oily movement of the water as its angle changed and we went bumping and twisting into the foaming vortex of the cataract, a boiling, thundering, world of white water. I took a quick glance at the two guides who crouched fore and aft with their long poles ready to lever the craft clear of rocks that broke the surface of the rapids. Their faces were set. Time after time a heave on the leading pole swung the canoe out of the danger line when too much turbulence showed the presence of a rock near the surface.

Time after time the frail hull was levered clear of rocks that would have split it in two, for the Missimi was thundering downhill beneath a smoking haze of spindrift, and a spill meant certain death in the rolling turmoil of the rapids. But I saw no worry in the hard set faces of the guides; occasionally they broke into shouts of triumphant hilarity and excitement, for it was a journey of immense exhilaration. Time after time the long craft was levered clear of sure destruction as it continued its twisting, bumping, pitching course.

For over half a mile the river roared along its cliff-walled channel, we were drenched to the skin and sometimes blinded by spray. Then the river slowed and widened into a foam-flecked pool where the outboard was rehoused and started. There were more rapids, but calm stretches grew ever longer and the cataracts became smaller. As we glided on I settled back to watch the passing of that enchanted world of rocks and grass and riverine plants that separate the river from the sombre depth of the dark Canadian timber.

For several miles we skimmed slowly over wide stretches of very shallow water where progress was as difficult as the passage through Hells Gorge had been; now the ever-present danger was of rubbing on the bottom. The water deepened again and normal progress was resumed. Quite unexpectedly—to me—as we rounded a bend two flag-poles came into view with the Canadian flag and the Stars and Stripes hanging limply together in the afternoon heat. Camp Missimi at last!

FIVE

THE MILLION DOLLAR POOL

Although I had grown to accept the beauty of the river scene after seeing so much splendour, the prospect of the stretch of water known as the 'million dollar pool' was none the less exciting. No railroad or highway had been driven through these parts and only a handful of guides, lumbermen and anglers had ever set eyes on this 'million dollar pool.' On either side of the immense stretch of water, steep hills clad in the variegated greens of larch, spruce, balsam, pine, poplar and sycamore towered above the ice-line to a thousand feet. Three islands green with spruce relieved the cobalt and turquoise pool. On a gentle slope opposite one of the islands, a clearing had been made, and on either side of its trim lawns, flew the flags of Canada and the United States that I had seen as we entered the pool. At the back of the lawns wooden steps led to a verandah gay with rambler roses.

My companions stopped the outboard motor and we made the last stage of our journey over the calm surface of the great pool. In the clear depths, I could see schools of salmon with tails and fins gently fanning, some of them maintained position or moved away from the passing shadow of the boat. Two bald eagles passed overhead curving an effortless path across the blue vault of the sky. A big fish leapt in an arc of flashing silver to hit the surface of the pool with a resounding smack. A startled moose left the water's edge to crash noisily away through the forest. We glided to a stop beside the beached canoes at the landing-stage.

There was no sign of life: during the heat of the afternoon guests and servants slept, relaxing before fishing in the cool of the evening. This was a good time to explore the camp. I visited the generator house, the fire house, office, first-aid station and the canoe sheds. Built into the steep bank was the snowhouse which during the previous winter had been filled with packed snow to preserve caught salmon against the heat of summer.

Insulated from warmth by the slope of the hill the snow remained unmelted throughout the summer, and salmon were kept fresh in its icy embrace. I tried the heavy door, and it creaked slowly back on its hinges. A clammy breath of cold air laced with a fishy smell hung for an instant like a miasma in the heat of the afternoon. In the frigid gloom I could see a dozen salmon laid out on the snow, the big fish that Goldup had talked about was not among them. Then slamming the door tight, I went to the smoke house where filleted salmon hung in the smoke that came from a fire built underground away from the hut, I saw that the smoke passed along a conduit to the base of the hut where bronzed, reddish fillets hung. I opened the door and when the smoke had cleared, it was obvious that there was no carcass of outstanding size here either, so I knew that the big fish was still at large and I hoped that it would remain uncaught until it reached the counting fence when I would be able to read its scales.

A gong sounded and I was invited to join the guides for a meal which I badly needed. Afterwards I was taken to the guests quarters to discuss the programme for the evening.

Harry B. Goldup sat on the verandah with five friends and as many glasses of whisky. As I approached I could hear them discussing Anglo-Canadian-American affairs, apparently oblivious to the supreme beauty of the Missimi pool in the evening light. Its clear turquoise waters,

'Green as a dream and deep as death'

wound between the little islands and the moss-covered reefs where the pool-bound salmon lay. The guides were busy preparing rods and choosing flies for the evening cast. Mr Goldup spotted me as I reached the steps.

'Brought that microscope,' he called.

'Yup, I've brought it,' I replied.

'That's fine. Tonight we'll show them a thing or two. You're coming out in my boat and I'm reckoning on yer bringing me luck . . . that big fellow is still around. I saw him only yesterday, he rose at my fly and took it, but smashed me to pieces with his first rush, took my brand-new Silver Doctor. But I've got a hunch that I'm gonna get that fly back. If I get into him again I'll know just how to handle things. He took me by surprise, went across the pool like a living torpedo and broke me, but if I get another chance . . .'

As subsequent events transpired Mr Goldup's hunch was right, he did get his fly back but not in the way that he imagined.

The guides had already reached the canoes, rods were put in place and engines prepared. Everyone mingled easily, millionaires and servants, round the landing-stage. It was a strange social phenomenon where two such groups of men could unite in such a free and happy corporate unit where laughter and leg pulling was given and taken on both sides.

The heat of the day had passed and already the surface of the long pool was broken by the rings of rising trout. One at a time the canoes left the landing-stage to skim over the surface of the water to some fancied position above or below the great pool.

Mr Goldup and I sat in the same boat and headed downstream until we came to a region of wide currents where, it was thought, the fish would be more alert than in the dead water of the pool. A heavy lead weight served as an anchor, and the long canoe was held gurgling in the centre of the current, I accepted one of Mr Goldup's cigars and sat back to watch, while Angus the guide began casting. Extra line was let out between each cast until the salmon fly was hitting the water ninety feet away. After three or four casts, the guide in the stern lifted his weight and allowed the canoe to run on for some yards, then Angus cast again. In this way we slowly descended the length of current, Angus doing all the skilled work of casting, while Goldup waited.

When we reached the deep water of the next pool Angus looked up at the clear blue sky and wrinkled his nose.

'No dam' good tonight, I guess, water's too clear, and there's not a breath of air to freshen up the surface.'

Harry Goldup shook with laughter and turned to me.

'Never met such a guy in all my life, biggest pessimist that ever held a rod, he's full of reasons why fish can't be caught. It's either too cold and the fish are too chilled to touch the fly, or it's too hot, like tonight, and the salmon are too listless and couldn't care less. If it's neither warm nor cold, it's too mild I guess or the wind'll be coming from the wrong quarter or there'll be too many clouds about. If there ain't any clouds, he'll be saying it's too clear for fishing. If the sky is overcast, it'll be too damn dull. Then there's the colour of the water, if it's a bit muddy the fish can't see the fly, if the water's clear, like tonight, they can see the tackle and it frightens 'em away.' I nodded my sympathy as he continued his good-natured harangue. 'Then of course there's the level of the water, I guess he thinks that's damned important, water must be at the right height, not too high or too low. If there's thunder in the air it's useless to try, and after the thunder's gone the fish are too scared. If an otter or a bear's swum over the river upstream, that'll put 'em right off. If a bear so much as puts his foot in the water old Angus'll tell you that all the salmon for a hundred yards or more downstream will be finished for the night.'

'Well that's right enough isn't it?' broke in the long-suffering Angus, 'nothing frightens salmon quicker than the smell of a bear. If he goes into the river to drink, the salmon get terrified, and you can pack up fishing for that day.'

I had never realised that a salmon's sense of smell was so highly developed, and I resolved to put it to the test. I pressed old Angus for further details. Our discussion was suddenly interrupted by the half splash of a rising salmon. It swirled on the surface, and disappeared with a flash and thump of the tail that echoed against the rocky walls of the pool, and a group of widening rings spread over the surface of the water. Angus stopped casting and sat down to light his pipe. 'Guess we'll give that fish a little minute or two to recover then he should take,' he said. After lighting up Angus turned and swung his rod to drop the fly well above the rise, and slowly whipped his way nearer to the spot where he thought the fish was resting. With the fourth cast the fly hit the water slightly beyond the spot. There was a moment's tension as we waited for the fish to take, then there was a gentle swirl and Angus struck. The rod bent into a quivering semicircle, and the tight line hissed away over the surface of the pool as the salmon made its first rush. Angus let it go until most of his line had run out. As he brought the check to bear, the salmon leapt to a height of six feet, fins extended, tail beating, its body a flashing arc of silver in the evening light.

Angus passed the rod to Harry Goldup who began to reel the salmon slowly in. The fish then saw the boat, and again rushed the full length of the line. As Goldup reeled in again, the salmon went down, sounding like a whale in its panic.

'Better not let 'im go too deep,' shouted Angus, 'probably making for a root where 'e'll smash you.'

The line went slack, but the fish was well hooked. It surfaced in a mad leap for freedom, then followed a succession of spectacular jumps but each jump was smaller than the previous one. Each time it was reeled in it came quietly, recovering its strength as it was drawn in, and time after time the line went screaming out as the fish made repeated runs for freedom. It was a big fish, and when it wanted to go its determined strength would have broken the tackle, had not Goldup played it skilfully.

Personally I felt few of the thrills that moved the other men. To me that salmon was hooked in the mouth and held on a tight line to fight out an uneven battle to an inevitable end.

Time after time the fish ran out to the full length of the line, and as often as it did so Goldup reeled it back in, protesting, lurching, leaping and fighting all the way. Gradually its struggles subsided and when it was no longer able to make its noble dash on catching sight of the canoe, Goldup reeled in, raising his rod higher as the great silver fish was drawn ever nearer to where Angus Frazer reached out with his net. The gallant fighter was spent, its spirit broken, and it floated in under the strain of the line, turning over to expose its silver side. Then it was lifted unprotesting in the embrace of the net, and dumped into the canoe, where it was dealt a quick blow at the base of the skull, and its life of adventure ended. She was a twenty-pound hen fish and perhaps the last survivor from a spawning six years before, maybe in a tiny tributary near the head waters of Missimi. She had returned to make her contribution with a roe of about sixteen thousand embryonic spawn to plant in the gravel of the tributary whose scent she sought. Her long journey had ended otherwise, and she lay inert on the floor of the boat. There was at least one member of the party who felt little pleasure in her killing.

Then we headed downstream and tried again in the fast water below the pool, but without success. Harry Goldup's nervous energy could not be contained in a small canoe when the salmon were reluctant to 'take.' He resented staying still for any length of time in one place, and so we returned early to the landing-stage.

If Goldup hated staying still for any length of time,

I was the direct opposite. For me, the fascinating sport of learning nature's secrets could only be practised by patient observation, and I longed to be alone at the edge of this wonderful pool. So making my excuses, and promising to see him later, I moved away into the undergrowth until I reached a rocky section at the head of the pool where I sat down to wait.

Everywhere the quiet peace of early August lay over the forest and the river, the feverish mating and breeding period of the birds in spring and early summer was over. Second broods had been reared by many birds and the song cadenzas which had rung out far and wide, had now ceased. It was the time when parent birds were free to enjoy the peace of August, the month of holiday and recuperation, a reward for their earlier work. Food was plentiful, insects and fruit were abundant, domestic responsibilities were over, and life was easy and good. August was the time when heavy feeding could begin, and banquets could go on with ever-growing richness into the ripened beauty of the fall, for by then a layer of fat would be laid over the bodies of birds and beasts to fortify them against winter's harsh privations. Whether the denizens of the forest stayed on and lived through the grim Canadian winter, or flew southward on a three thousand mile migration to winter on the plains of South America, a great reserve of tissue in flesh and fat would be needed.

So as I chose my observation point overlooking the head of 'million dollar pool' and settled down to watch. The silence of August lay over the river and the trees. Occasionally the voice of the white throat sparrow, whose long drawn monotonous whee-ee-ee, in the minor key expressed unutterable sadness, as it echoed along the dim glades of the forest. The notes served only to accentuate the solitude of the place. The bird's young had flown and I knew that its song was no longer needed, and its continual persistence began to irritate me.

My attention was distracted by a small animal moving among the rocks at the river's edge. I remained as still as the mossy rocks on which I sat. It was a mink, hunting the riverside pools for small fish. Its long body moved with extreme grace, and its fur shone with a lustre never seen on cured skins. Then it came to a pool where a shoal of minnows swam, it saw them, flattened itself and watched the fish as a sheepdog watches sheep. Then it crept like a brown snake to the edge of the pool, took silently to the water and swam round the minnows several times. Gradually it closed in as the minnows lost their fear of the unhurried movements of the brown shape above them. When the mink judged the nearest minnow to be within its reach, it flashed at it, killed it, and dropped it at the edge of the pool, then resumed its quiet circling again. In this way it caught six minnows and dropped each at the pool's edge. Then it tried to pick them all up, but its mouth was too small, and it finally carried off four of the fish into the shelter of the undergrowth.

The surface of the great pool showed the rings of rising trout, and high overhead the first night hawk sounded the whirring roar of its dive at an evening moth as it left the cover of the pines.

Salmon leapt occasionally, sometimes they rose and curled on the surface to grab impulsively at a passing fly. At other times they came high out of the water in the beauty of natural freedom unhampered by the maddening sting of a barbed hook in the mouth and the dragging weight of a line. These jumps were a joy to watch, but they may have been caused by the irritating presence of fresh-water lice on the salmon's gills, and the jumps were probably the fish's frantic efforts to shake the clinging parasites away. Though uncommon in maritime rivers, lice sometimes gather in the depths of quiet pools, and when salmon linger too long among them, infestation occurs.

Suddenly there was a bigger flash of silver as an enormous salmon shot out of the water to a height of around eight feet, and I knew that this was the giant 'sixty pounder.' It flashed into the air, body swaying, with fins extended and tail ringing, before curling over to fall again and hit the water with a solid smack.

To witness the free leap of a sixty-pound salmon is a thrill given only to few observers. It is a great experience and I felt that the excitement of that memorable day could go no further. Before the light faded completely into the tranquil August night the big fish leapt again at the same spot and I was more than satisfied. Finally the black flies and mosquitoes won and I had to turn away from the pool and return to the fishing camp, where Mr Goldup persuaded me to produce the microscope and tell the story of detecting the age of a salmon to the distinguished gathering of guests.

On the following morning I woke long before the camp was astir and slipped out of my bunk and returned to the top end of the silent pool. The usual translucence of the pre-dawn sky was absent on this occasion, an oppressive greyness was everywhere, and it seemed as if the long spell of fine weather was about to end.

For several weeks the lone fire watchers at their look-out posts on the mountain tops had been scanning their vast arboreal vistas with increasing vigilance. One spark in the drought could have caused untold damage to the timber crop. Rain was needed over the entire Province to reduce fire danger and freshen up the rivers to enable the salmon to move out of the stagnant pools.

I knew that the arrival of rain would swell the river sufficiently to deepen the rock shallows above the pool, and enable the shoals of salmon to pass on upstream. They would negotiate the cataracts of Hell's Gorge, and I should intercept the sixty-pounder at the counting fence, before letting it move on up to the lake and the remote spawning grounds beyond.

As I emerged from the undergrowth at the head of the pool, the resin-scented air seemed heavy with the threat of approaching thunder and the world of nature seemed to be holding its breath, waiting in a silence of unearthly stillness. No daybreak wind accompanied the eerie light of dawn as it spread westward over the silent forests. With the strangely diffused light and the lack of breeze, I could see clearly into the pool where the salmon lay. They too sensed the approaching storm and perhaps instinctively knew that the time of waiting would soon be over, the shallows would deepen with rain, the way ahead would be open, and the long migration could be resumed again.

As the top end of the pool continued to thicken with salmon I crept forward over the rock shelf until I was able to look more closely into the water. As I watched the gentle movements that propelled the migrants on, I seemed to feel the grim determination of their purpose. Their movement had been halted by drought, now the sensitive responses of the fish to atmospheric change told them to be ready to move. Gently fanning with tail and fins, they moved their spotted, streamlined bodies, mouths opening and closing rhythmically as they breathed. The numbers thickened one behind the other, one above the other, and one beside the other. Looking along their ranks I could see the scars of many adventures. Tooth marks of otters and seals, the weals left by the meshes of nets, bruises resulting from ill-timed jumping at waterfalls, and some fish showed the first pale signs of insidious fungus on their heads. I knew that such fish would never regain the sea. Some of the bigger hens showed by their more heavily spotted heads that they had spawned before, and were moving up-river a second time.

I continued to lie on the warm rock ledge and hardly dared to breathe or blink for fear of disturbing the assembling salmon. There was no excitement between the sexes as they held their places and waited in the gentle flow of the warm water from the rocky shallows. Occasionally a fish would turn and disappear swiftly into the lower reaches of the pool, like a person in a queue who suddenly decides to wait no longer.

Suddenly my heart started pounding as I saw the giant fish of the previous evening move silently and majestically into view between the ranks of waiting salmon. This was fantastic—of all the luck! She was a henfish of around sixty pounds weight and her head and tail seemed small by comparison with her body. What she lacked in the shapely beauty of the younger hens, she made up for in size. In her I sensed an almost limitless reserve of stored vitality—apparent in the rounded curve of her back, and the deeply curving sweep of her stomach which already showed the distention of a heavy cargo of spawn. She rose slowly from the green depths of the pool and came to rest among the other salmon like a liner taking its position in a crowded convoy of cargo ships.

The giant's head was more richly spotted than any of the second spawners, which meant that she was probably a third spawner. How my fingers itched for the chance to have one of her scales to learn something of the secret of her life and see the number of spawning marks, but I would have to await her arrival at the counting fence twenty-five miles upstream.

I was so completely absorbed in my observations of the pool and its contents that I failed to notice the first flash of lightning in the darkening sky but the low growl of thunder that followed it left me in no doubt that rain was on the way. Then the first breeze of the coming storm passed gently through the aspen leaves, it ruffled the glassy surface of the pool, the fish below were lost to view, and the idyll of the morning was over.

I stood up and looked about me, and in the growing whisper of the wind in the forest I could hear a fresh note, the rustle of rain falling on foliage. The vanguard of the storm crashed down the wooded slope, hissed over the wide pool and went on across the wilderness, and the wonder and beauty of the valley was blotted out as the lowering curtain of clouds merged with the rising mantle of steam.

I made a hasty return to camp, and for the remainder of the day stayed indoors as the rain continued to fall and the river turned steadily browner with the rising flood.

SIX

SWIMMING THE GAUNTLET OF DEATH

In the lukewarm depths of 'million dollar pool' the salmon schools were growing restless. Born to a life-long heritage of adversity, the tireless fish had been obliged to accept the temporary hold up. Many had been pool-bound for at least two weeks since their arrival. At night they glided about the water like restless ghosts, and at sunrise shoaled up nose to tail in the deeper runs. Every morning found the numbers greater and this was most marked on the morning when the rain came. Every salmon for miles downstream had felt the atmospheric change, and the urge to travel had been stimulated.

As the giant henfish reached the head of the pool and rose between the waiting squadrons of her kind, she felt in every nerve of her body, the change that percolated through the water from the air. Though deep in the water, they were as sensitive to the effect of wind as any mammal of the land, and when the rain first lashed the pool it sent a ripple of excitement through the waiting fish.

Gradually the cooling fragrance of the rain diffused in the hated warmth of the pool and the salmon felt it and rose to bask in its refreshing sweetness. The cold rain sank, the warm water rose and the gentle displacements added to the excitement in the eager fish. As the hours passed, the swollen tributaries of the watershed poured from the forests by a thousand singing cascades to freshen the river and excite the waiting spawners with its ever-growing coolness, taste, and smell of the shallows for which they longed.

As the day advanced, the river took on a milky tint, which gradually darkened as more surface soil was washed by the rain-fed rivulets. The salmon smelt the odours of the land, and as the daylight faded their eagerness mounted, the shallow trickle over the flat rock above the pool grew deeper, and for the waiting migrants, the gateway to the upper Missimi was opening.

It was the small three-pound grilse that went first; with backs out of the water they wriggled vigorously over the slab until they came to deeper water, and for them the way ahead was clear.

When the effect of the day's rain reached the big pool, the level rose quickly and the bigger salmon went sliding over the rock wall in the darkness of the rushing water as it surged and gurgled with its burden of torn off slime and weed and suspended grit, mud, twigs and pine needles.

Throughout the hours of darkness on that night of spate, the salmon of 'million dollar pool' slipped quietly away on their journey upstream. The guides knew now that the pool was empty, fishing would be useless and it was now the turn of the anglers to become bored with waiting.

The giant hen fish went over soon after the grilse, and shot across the shallows until she came to the deeper water. As she glided through the darkness, she felt the same relief at moving on that any traveller feels after a long delay. Her powerful tail kept her gliding easily forward, and one after another she passed the straggling grilse as they went listlessly on from one resting-place to another.

The water was heavily coloured, and throughout the night the big hen moved in total darkness. She saw nothing of the river rocks, submerged tree trunks, root masses and other obstacles, but she never touched one in that Stygian gloom. She swam with her nose seeking the direct flow of the current and the slightest turbulence in the water caused by a root or boulder reacted on the sense organs that lay along the lateral-line on either side of her body. Every projecting rock or stone affected the current's flow, and for her was easily avoided. The nerve endings on her flanks kept her informed of the flow of the water about her, if the flow was equal on either side of her, she was automatically in the middle of the current where her progress was assured. So throughout the hours of darkness the lengthening shoals of salmon moved steadily and safely between the rocks until daylight found them strung out in the long pools below Hell's Gorge. As the light increased, the holding pools which had been empty of salmon for several weeks, now held their quota of resting fish. The questing urge kept them ever eager to be moving on against the current, but with greater caution as the light had come. Throughout the day they continued to make furtive movements from one pool to the next. As one salmon would glide from a current into a resting place, the fish in possession of the resting place would move on and displace the salmon ahead. Nearly a thousand salmon which had left 'million dollar pool' on the previous night, were strung out over a three mile stretch of the river below the gorge. The fish which had entered the river last, and suffered least in the warm stagnation of the pools, now took the lead, the giant hen among them. The roaring sound of the cataract grew ever louder as they moved towards it. The highly oxygenated waters acted as a stimulant and the movements of the fish became faster and more purposeful. This supercharging of energy was needed in the twisting roaring whiteness through which the leading salmon sliced their way. Resting places were few, and as the leaders needed longer rests, they were caught up and the quieter eddies became thick with gasping fish. The big hen with the extra leverage of her long body, drew ahead of the others and reached a comparatively quiet harbour of refuge where she spread her fins and rested on the bottom to gulp rapidly until her breathing eased. Twice in previous years she had mounted the rapids of the gorge and on each occasion she had rested in this place and dreadful things had happened. As she lay and recovered from her exertions, the previous experiences were vaguely recalled and she pressed her great bulk lower on the rocky floor, and the swirling snowstorm of bubbles passed continuously along her speckled flanks, and her camouflage became absolute. Other salmon caught her up, waited awhile, then shot away into the twisting current, but she remained as immovable as a pulp log sunk and wedged in a rocky cleft. The froth of the cataract swirled over her hiding place and thickened into a creamy paste of turning foam, and she lay hidden beneath it. More salmon came up, waited and passed on. Then in the water came the first scent and taste of salmon blood, and with it the sinister and terrifying scent of bears. The great fish had instinctively remembered a previous experience with a bear that had nearly caught her at the killing place half-way up the gorge.

It was probable that the previous days heavy rain served to remind the bears that the river would rise and enable the pool-bound shoal of salmon to move into the gorge. Several groups of black bears had taken up positions on projecting rocks which commanded a view of the passing fish.

Black bears normally took no part in salmon killing in the Maritimes, but here on Missimi River the pattern of their behaviour changed. At certain seasons when a big run of salmon went up in the wake of a summer flood, the bears of the neighbourhood gathered on the rocks for the period of the run, and like their cousins of the far north-west they took to catching salmon. In spring and autumn the floods were always too heavy for them, it was only at certain times in summer when the water was low enough, that the invisible passage of salmon tempted the bears to leave their dense woodland homes to try their clumsy skill in the river.

Several had come out of the forest during that night, to sit and wait beside the tumbling waters. Some had waded on to rocks that stood out of the current. As the first salmon slid along the green spillway of a run, a watching bear made a lightning scoop with his paw, but missed, the salmon flashed into view and was gone in a gush of silver that excited the other bears as they stood at their watching places. Then other salmon appeared and the killers were busy. Occasionally a bear would scoop a salmon out of the water and kill it, but many fish got back.

The omnivorous bears were ill-equipped for catching

salmon, and for every one that was caught, many escaped unharmed to carry on upstream, but many were lacerated along their flanks by bear claws and sent floating down with the current to die slowly at the foot of the gorge. It was clumsy slaughter but to the black bears it was sport. Like fishermen, the enjoyment of the sport was more important than eating the kill. Parts of some of the fish were eaten, several half-eaten fish with blood and scales littered the rocks behind each waiting bear. A pair of bald eagles alighted and gorged themselves, and a fox returning to its lair with a blue jay in its mouth, dropped the bird in haste and dashed in to help clear up the carnage. Then came the cleverest thieves of all, a family of ravens whose harsh excited cries informed the forest world that something unusual was afoot. A wolverine, asleep in his den half a mile away, heard the noise and lifted his ugly little head to listen. The excitement in the voices of the ravens told him all that was necessary, he was a specialist in death, the undertaker of the forest. Wherever there was death, it was the giant weasle's business to be there. The Indians called him the devil dog. He moved out of his den and immediately went into his characteristic gait, a shuffling, bouncing, lumbering gallop like no other creature. Although little larger than a heavy fox he and his kind were the undisputed rulers of the dense Canadian wilds from the Gulf of St Lawrence to beyond the Arctic circle.

In the rocky glen the sport of the bears was improving, their skill at scooping out the passing salmon had returned, and they were all set for a day of slaughter. They were so preoccupied with their lust that they failed to notice the sudden flight of the fox, which would normally have given cause for suspicion. The crafty fox had winded the approaching killer and fled before his arrival.

The joy of the bears was brought to a speedy conclusion by the appearance of the bloodthirsty wolverine, whose small black face displayed an expression of demoniac rage that could terrorise a timber wolf. At the approach of a wolverine no killer of the forest waits to dispute the issue. The big black bears were no exception, they saw the dreaded loping gait of the giant weasle and turned like a gang of poachers at the sudden arrival of a warden. There followed a panic-stricken rush to cross the rapids, and several bears were whirled downstream to be swept among the ascending salmon which had gathered into eddies where they lay too frightened to advance any further in the danger-reeking water. The bears had lost all interest in the salmon and were concerned only with reaching the opposite bank where they quickly disappeared into the bush.

The wolverine, who lived in a state of perpetual hunger, gorged himself on the plunder of the bears, and as he tore and munched at the red flesh of the salmon, the silver grey shapes of the shoal survivors slid silently past the danger spot, and one after another came to the calm seclusion of the peace above the gorge.

The wolverine whose timely arrival had removed the gauntlet of death from the path of the coming salmon, continued to eat his fill. Finally he proceeded to bury the carcass of each fish in a different part of the surrounding forest after first defiling it with his nauseating scent to render it unpalatable to any other creature.

Throughout the day the big hen fish lay inert and tense, hidden under the turning canopy of foam in her sheltered eddy. She had often been crowded by her fellows as they waited and queued on their journey up-stream. But many had dropped back, maimed and dying, with blood leaking from torn stomach wounds where the bears had ripped. The old fish had survived more disasters through her habit of hiding for longer periods when terror threatened, than the other fish.

The run of salmon had long ceased, but still the hen fish waited until at last the sun went down and darkness filled the noisy gorge. Then purposefully she moved out and thruddled her way powerfully through the onrush of the falling spate until at last she reached the peace of the wooded valley beyond.

The roaring sound of the waters at the head of the gorge fell gradually away as she glided forward through the darkening river. The nerve-endings along her lateral lines took over control, and like an automatic pilot, kept her on her course. The quiet rhythmic beating of her muscles kept her big black triangular tail moving throughout the greater part of the night, as tireless and efficient as the wings of a long-distance flying migrant bird. On several occasions during the night she caught up and passed weakening salmon which had been bruised by the clumsy bears, and escaped although doomed to suffer a lingering death through the eventual growth of fungus which would start by the entry of the deadly bacilli in the lacerations of their skin. She passed them with complete indifference, their wounds were no concern of hers, for her the task of safely burying her precious cargo of spawn was the only reason for her journey and her life, and nothing would deflect her from that purpose. She swam on until at last she caught up with the four-year-old grilse at the tail end of the shoal. They were fish which had reached the smolt stage as three-year-olds, and migrated down to the St Lawrence Gulf to winter off the shores of Cape Breton Island where they had grown to a weight of three pounds. They were now returning under the powerful call of their natal stream in whose zone of influence they had probably lingered throughout their first winter in the sea.

As the mighty hen fish overtook them, the young males surged forward on either side of her like small sharks about a giant whale, but they could not maintain her speed and after a mile she had shaken them off.

The flood water passed and the river was clear again, and as the sun rose over the eastern hills, the shadows of the tall spruce trees that lined the bank were thrown across the water and the fish moved over bars of light and shadow on the river bed. After the night's gloom, the effect of this brilliant light on the shallow clear water disturbed them even more than the presence of a pair of ospreys that followed overhead and dived occasionally on the grilse.

What the two great fish hawks saw from the sky was a moving procession of nature in all its freedom and magnificence, hundreds of Atlantic salmon travelling steadily up the valley towards their goal in the spruce glens of the high mountains. The ocean cavalcade of anadromous fish were exposed to constant danger as they moved through the strange unpalatable element of river water to fulfil the purpose of their lives.

Female Atlantic salmon. Just prior to spawning. (*Department of Fisheries of Canada*)

Male Atlantic salmon. Note hooked jaw of near-spawning fish. (*Department of Fisheries of Canada*)

SEVEN

THE CAPTIVE GIANT

The strong sunlight of the bright New Brunswick sky soon checked the forward movement of the fish, and they gradually halted in separate groups and lay resting in pools where the water was deep enough to give them the confidence of concealment. The giant hen had caught up with a group of eight big salmon in whose company she felt more at ease than with any others, her presence too seemed to act as a unifying force on them, restoring a feeling of confidence which they had lost during her absence on the journey from the rapids. The cock fish seemed particularly pleased at her return among them, and closed in on either side of her although the mating urge as yet lay dormant in the waiting fish. As the day wore on, the nine big salmon remained poised in line astern off the centre of the current, keeping their stations at slightly different levels with gentle movements of tail and fins.

Many months before, there had been eighteen of them, they all had come together on the distant Atlantic feeding grounds far to the north of the Grand Banks of Newfoundland.

Where the Labrador current met the warm Gulf Stream, a shark caught one of them, and almost within sight of the coast of Newfoundland, a grey seal took another. The sixteen survivors eventually reached close in to the rocky shores of Cape Breton Island where one of the school swam into the trap-net of Daniel O'Coin off the estuary of the Margaree River. The others swam on, tasting and smelling the scents of the rivers where their zones of influence floated over the Gulf of St Lawrence. Off Prince Edward Island, three salmon of the school were caught by the gills in the mile long floating drift-nets, while the rest passed safely underneath. The twelve survivors merged with the growing numbers of potential spawners, and every fish in that mighty cavalcade tasted and sampled the rivers that lay on the sea. In the sense organs of every salmon lay the dormant power to recognise the taste and scent of its birth river. One river after another projected its scents to the passing ocean roamers, a call for which they waited and to which they responded with the yearning of the returning migrant.

That salmon follow these floating streams of river water, is clearly proved at the ancient fish traps of Goldcliff on the north shore of the Bristol Channel in Wales. When a north-east wind blows off the Monmouthshire coast, no salmon are caught in the traps because the water of the rivers Wye and Severn, which the fish are following, drift further out in the channel under the influence of the off-shore wind. Only when a south-west wind keeps the river water running along the shore are the salmon caught.

Thus in the ever-narrowing channel of the brackish waters of Missimi estuary, the giant hen and her travelling companions moved in and out with the tides for several days while preparing themselves for their new fresh-water environment and awaiting the courage to face the dangers that lurked on either side of the waterway. Over seventy licensed trap-nets stood out from both banks, and a heavy toll was taken of salmon that left the centre of the current.

They glided leisurely from pool to pool usually in the coolness and safety of the dark. Suddenly one salmon rose irritably at a moving fly only to find, to its terror, that the fly had two barbed hooks and a crippling line with death at the other end.

Bears had accounted for two more. Of this original company of eighteen splendid adult salmon who started on the ocean route for home, half of them had already been sacrificed.

The nine survivors now lay with heads up-stream, mouths opening and closing as though chewing the cud like nine cows waiting in the wind for milking time. Thus the salmon waited until dark, then one at a time they all moved slowly on again, and the cool caressing thrill of the current passed over their scaly sides from which the steel blue beauty of the sea was already beginning to fade. Nearly three weeks had passed since they left the sea, and the guanine deposit on the scales already showed the first faint traces of a tarnish, that would increase in the weeks that were to come.

Owing to the freshness of the flood water they moved on with ease in the darkness until suddenly an unnatural disturbance in the water brought the leading salmon to a stop, pectoral fins extended, and tails curved stiffly in readiness for instant flight. Thus they waited poised, eternally suspicious.

The old hen moved slowly backwards, she had long outgrown her sense of curiosity at strange things, for her they were always better avoided. At the first hint of danger, she was the first to flash away. Courage could willingly be relegated to the males, for her there was a direct responsibility to the forty-eight thousand potential salmon which she carried in her spawn. Of all this she had no knowledge but behind her instinctive female fear lay the infinite wisdom of the master planner. It was the accepted duty of females to escape with their young and leave the males to face danger and death, for the males were more easily expendable and of no direct loss to the race.

In the darkness ahead of them, a close-set mesh of vertical rods stretched away on either side, and through the rods the current hummed and whined.

The nine fish lay still, tense and watchful for several minutes until one of them moved slowly forward under the frames of the counting fence, the others followed until their noses touched the bars. The old salmon hung back and waited while her fellows inched slowly along the base of the fence in the direction in which they were supposed to go.

The fence had been built across the river at an angle, and as each waiting salmon adjusted its position in the current, it moved ever nearer to the cage entrance where an inviting flow of water tempted them into the pen.

One by one the eight big salmon entered, and as a last sheep follows its fellows into a crowded pen, so the giant salmon moved in through the wire opening to join her travelling companions inside the trap.

On the previous day I had returned to Camp Musquash and my first job was to open the salmon trap. On the following morning I went out as usual in the hope that a good run of fish had started in the wake of the flood.

I was not disappointed. The sight that lay below me made my pulse race with pleasure, for many of the big salmon which had been so desperately sought by the millionaire anglers some days before, now lay in crowded ranks entirely at my command. As I glanced along the spotted ranks of fish, I saw in the furthest corner, with dorsal fin half out of the water, the giant salmon.

I climbed very slowly down among them and started work on the smaller grilse, until only the big ones were left. I felt reluctant to face the problem of taking hold of the giant, because her violent struggles might result in bruising or cutting her skin in the confined space of the cage. This could lead to a fungus infection and a long slow death. I stood up to straighten my aching back, and while the passing water gurgled round my legs I pondered on the best way to tackle the job. Gradually I moved nearer to where she lay until at last I was kneeling in the water almost within touching distance of the black and red mottling of her scales. The strait-jacket that held the normal salmon was useless for this fish.

As I knelt there in my rubber waders behind the bars of the cage in the deep seclusion of the forest, I quietly floated the glass-bottomed bucket round until the salmon's head was framed in the circle of glass and every detail of its head and face was clearly visible. She may have been completely indifferent to my presence, or too paralysed with fear to move, the strange unwinking eye into which I looked, held no recognisable expression but her feelings were betrayed by the two big pectoral fins that lay behind the gills, they were stiffly spread and ready for instant movement, the fin rays were distended like an open fan. The spotted gill covers moved slowly in unison with the opening and closing of her big white mouth as she breathed. Then I noticed that fixed to the gristle of her almost toothless lower jaw were four anglers' salmon flies which the great fish had broken loose to carry off the barbed torture in her mouth. The colour in three of the hackles was faded and the metal parts already showed signs of rusting, mute testimony to the agony so often left in the name of sport to fester the flesh of hunted creatures.

I climbed out of the cage and returned to the cabin where I nailed three pieces of wood together to serve as an outsize strait-jacket to contain the big hen. I also picked up a pair of pliers for the awkward operation of extracting the fly hooks.

After a quick breakfast I returned to the cage where she still lay like a long dark shadow under the rippling water in the corner. I approached slowly using the same caution as before, then with infinite slowness, lowered the long strait-jacket over the five feet of her silver-plated muscle. The great Missimi giant was a captive.

'So far so good,' I mumbled to myself as I knelt on the long box and bent forward until I could see the dark snout projecting from one end. Then, with the help of the pliers, I cut and extracted the rusty barbed hooks away from her lips and transferred them to the wooden framework of the cage. It was only with difficulty that I could recognise them as a Silver Doctor, Green Highlander, Black Dose and Durham Ranger. Goldup's hunch that he would retrieve his Silver Doctor would come true; I intended to post it on to him. Then I tagged her and plucked some scales from her shoulder and put them into an envelope. She was able to go now, so I slowly lifted the strait-jacket and sat back on my heels to study her once more, but for some reason I was strangely reluctant to open the cage door and allow her to continue her journey. Over the scales lay a faint tinge of copper, the sure sign that she had spawned before. I had previously sought in vain over all the salmon which had passed since my arrival at Musquash for the rare coppery tinge of the second spawner, but there had been none until this one, and I resolved to keep her for a little while.

I took the scales for examination under the microscope. They were the biggest which I had ever handled, and under the lens I gradually pieced together the outline of her life.

From the concentration of small rings near the scale centre, it was obvious that she had spent three years in the river before reaching the smolt stage and leaving for the sea. Sudden widening of the rings showed fast growth in the rich feeding of the first summer at sea, then a gradual closing of the rings showed the first sea winter. She then grew rapidly again in the following summer, and this was followed by a sudden closing of the growth rings to form a dark circular scar, the first spawning mark at the age of five years. Then followed the rapid growth marks of two sea summers and the slower growth marks of two sea winters. The rings then merged again to form a second dark spawning mark bolder and more jagged than the first, which told of her second journey up the Missimi at the age of seven. I looked long at this tell-tale scar as I followed its dark trail round the perimeter of the seven-year period. In my imagination I saw her trapped beneath the winter ice, waiting in its black oblivion from autumn until spring without food. When the break up of spring ice freed her at last, she dropped back eastwards with the dying and the mending kelts to the happy hunting ground of the ocean for a third recovery. To the far off elixir of salmon life, where the young and old of all the silver race of Salar, from Biscay to the White Sea or from Maine to Labrador, go to feed and grow again to greater size in the healing feeding miracle of the sea's renaissance.

The evidence was clearly printed on the scale for anyone who had the knowledge and the eyes to read. Then I tried another scale under the microscope and the identical life history was revealed in the same detail. Beyond the second spawning scar at seven years of age, I saw two more sea summers of steady growth with two sea winters of limited growth beside them. The giant fish was nine years old at the time of her capture for marking.

Three times she had left the shores of Canada for her home in the North Atlantic, and three times including this year she had returned from the ocean depths to spawn amidst the forested mountain grandeur of New Brunswick. A flood of sentimental warmth towards the fish welled up within me, a feeling which had little to do with the work of scientific investigation to which I had committed myself. It was a feeling of human sympathy for a fish which for nine years had conquered all but impossible odds. To me she was the queen of the river.

EIGHT

THE LEAPING PLACE

Throughout the day the nine big salmon lay in the cage patiently awaiting the coming of night, and that evening I opened the gate and saw them shoot away upstream. Then I started off by canoe until I came to the waterfalls where I thought that the bears might be waiting at their catching places.

It was dark when I reached the gorge and beached the canoe, and continued on foot among the giant boulders, yelling to announce my presence to any bears that may have come before me. It was a weird and dangerous place to spend the night, but I felt that once the salmon had passed the falls and gained the lake they would be safe. I saw no sign of bears, but my shouting might have scared them off, and throughout the short hours of the summer night I patrolled the falls and heard the frequent splashes as the salmon ascended among the crashing waters. At one point I had the satisfaction of seeing the white flash of a body almost five feet in length, leap high above the gleaming curve of the river where it roared over a ledge fully six feet above the seething pool. When the first traces of daylight filtered into the glen, I was able to watch the full display of salmon courage. From the milky depths below the falls the fish could have had no knowledge that a leap of six feet was needed to span the obstacle that barred their route. Five minutes would pass with no movement, then a long dark shape would spring from that seething cauldron, then others would leap in quick succession, as though each salmon waited in the bubbling thunder for a leader to make the first jump. They had no knowledge of where to leap, they left the water on a blind instinctive urge, up into the unknown. Many leapt too far away and fell short, others leapt at a more acute angle and hit the falls, to be swept back among the waiting fish. Some leapt too close to the rocky walls on either side, and were bounced backwards off the dripping moss. One landed on a ledge of rock and struggled frantically until it died, another landed on the same ledge but the slippery body of the first fish enabled the second one to slide back into the pool to try again: the first fish had not died in vain. Those that jumped at the correct angle from the right place with sufficient power reached the crest of the waterfall, and with a violent wriggle disappeared upstream. As each successful jump was completed I could not help feeling a joy and satisfaction similar to that which the salmon may have felt as they journeyed on, bearing my numbered tags away into the unknown.

When the jumping ceased I returned to the beached canoe and paddled back to camp for breakfast, after which I planned to return to the falls with a rope in order to climb down to retrieve the dead salmon, for my night's vigil aroused the prospect of fried cutlets from the fish which had stranded itself.

On reaching the place once more, I tied one end of the rope to a larch stem and dangled the other end over the wet and slippery wall of rock. I climbed down easily enough and reached the ledge beside the dead salmon.

I tied the head and tail together and attached it to my belt to leave both hands free for the climb. It was a tricky job on the slime-covered ledge with the roaring falls beside me, and the boiling pool below sending up clouds of mist and spindrift. The climb up was more difficult than the climb down for the greasy footholds could not be trusted and the weight of the fish on my belt added to my difficulty. It was a great relief at last when my feet gripped the drier moss above the gorge and I regained the larch tree.

Back at the cabin the smell and sound of salmon frying in the pan soon made the effort seem well worth the trouble. As I breakfasted I pondered on the movements of the huge third spawner which had so captured my thoughts on the previous day. In my imagination I saw her and her companions resting throughout the bright period of daylight under a tangle of tree roots in the shade of the spruce trees that lined the bank. As the evening shadows deepened they would move away from the shelter of the roots to glide one at a time through the cool flow of the water of dim rock pools and shallow gravelly reaches. At last they would pass the place where the Boston poachers had hung their net, and immediately beyond, the river widened to form the lower end of Lake Missimi. Once in the lake they would be safe for a while.

As the schools of salmon left the head-on current of the river and reached the placid water of the lake, they slowed down and rested in long lines and shoals along the edge as though uncertain of their route. There was still no urgency about this summer run, for spawning time was yet far off, and in the deep calm of the lake a great peace and security awaited them.

In one secluded backwater near the waiting salmon, a family of beavers was already at work repairing their winter lodge and laying in a store of twigs and green shoots on which to feed throughout the coming winter. They worked quietly with unhurried thoroughness all through the night, for them, too, there was no urgency, for winter was far off, yet in obedience to the prompting of instinct they could not resist the urge to cut and carry twigs of maple and poplar to the food store at the base of the lodge.

Time after time the big furry animals surfaced near their pyramid of sticks and mud that stood out like an island of drift-wood in the middle of the backwater. They swam slowly and leisurely to the bank, and with hardly a ripple moved out among the lakeside foliage to gnaw off a branch of aspen from the poplar tree which they had felled some days before. They tugged it to the water's edge with a strength that seemed impossible for their size. Then, quietly entering the water and, half turning on their sides, they swam out to the lodge with the branch held clenched in strong yellow teeth, where it was added to the store of winter food. Throughout the lower Missimi, people held the firm belief that if the beavers started storing in August, a long hard winter would follow. They would say that a twig or branch once cut by the teeth of a beaver would never float but remain submerged until required.

Time after time the tireless workers passed and repassed each other on the surface of the water and swam endlessly to and fro throughout the darkest hours of the night. The backwater in which they worked formed a half circular bay, and round its landward edge the silhouette of spruce and poplars stood dark against the starlight. Over all the dim arboreal world of the vast Canadian wild there was silence. But it was silent only to man, to the creatures of the wild, movement went on continuously, and where there was movement there were sounds, both near and far. The working beavers, for all their tireless industry, read every sound for what it was; the whispering winnow in the wing beats of passing water fowl that grew rapidly fainter until a distant hiss announced their alighting on the surface of the lake; the gentle footfalls of deer and the sounds of their browsing; the moose stepping out of the lake made sucking noises as he lifted his hooves from the mud of the lily pads on which he had been feeding. The owl who lived on rodents, heard the movement of a distant vole. He spread his wings, and with the aid of downy silencers on every feather, flew in deadly silence straight to his mark, a tiny squeak acknowledged the ensuing drama. Silence returned.

It was the silence of planned killing that went on at every point in the forest. Into this world of never ending hunger came the hungerless salmon from the ocean route, and their numbers grew as the night wore on until at last all the fish which had left 'million dollar pool' and survived the bears' attack, lay resting in shoal formation in the sanctuary of the lake in the silence of night.

For the salmon, as for the beavers, the silent waterways through the forest were the busy thoroughfares of existence where seclusion was sought from man, the one great common enemy of all the world of nature. The beavers worked for personal survival in the coming winter, and the salmon worked for race survival in the ages of future time just as salmon had swum the gauntlet of Missimi's dangers in the past to enable the great shoal to live and reach the lake at the end of the summer to pass on the torch of life to salmon millions of the future.

As one fish felt the tingling itch of lice about its gills, it leapt high out of the water to fall back with a resounding smack in an attempt to remove the irritation. The beavers heard the smack on the water and reacted instinctively, diving beneath the surface and streaking for the safety of their lodge. What they had heard was identical to the warning tail slap made by a beaver when danger threatens. Work was suspended for the night, and a prolonged grooming session of wet fur was maintained until the red dawn came over the tree-fringed rim of the lake, and the beavers went to sleep.

NINE

INCIDENT AT THE COUNTING FENCE

Back at Camp Musquash in the days that followed, I maintained my watch at the counting fence, and records were carefully kept. Visitors were few but none the less welcome in my self-imposed exile. There was one exception to those whom I welcomed, a group of French Canadian lumbermen called in during a week-end, and after displaying a morbid interest in the working of the fence tried to bribe me into letting them have some fish. We nearly came to blows and it would have been pretty tough for me if we had. I had been given strict orders to keep the cage door locked each night, this had often puzzled me, but after this visitation the reason was all too obvious, and locking up became a nightly ceremony.

The idea of taking a fish for my own use had never occurred to me, particularly in view of the gossip which I knew was going on among the villagers and townsfolk further down the valley. The low water of late August had already given poachers many opportunities of taking salmon out of the pools by night, netting, jigging and explosives had been used and damaged fish later betrayed the evidence of such methods. Public opinion was aroused to such an extent that one of the local newspapers commented on the work of the poachers and the inability of the fishery wardens to put a stop to it. It was inevitable that the salmon research station at the old lumber camp should be included in these suspicions, and it was mentioned in the newspaper article together with the depredations of the poachers. Ignorant criticisms were levelled at the idea of catching salmon in a cage and branding them for life by attaching a metal plate which, it was claimed, would interfere with their movements in the water.

'It has been alleged,' stated the article, 'that severe damage has been caused to our Atlantic salmon and that death often follows their passage through the fence.' The article went on to point out to its readers that 'the liberty of free-moving fish had never been officially interfered with in this part of Canada before, and the usefulness of the counting fence is questioned.' It was concluded with the pious editorial hope that 'a complete investigation will be undertaken to look into the situation and see what action should be taken. Members of Angling Associations, Fishing Camp owners and all others concerned, should conduct an on-the-spot investigation into the procedure at the counting fence.'

I received a copy of the article with a note warning me to expect further developments.

It was perfectly obvious that the article had been inspired by the views of people who could not believe that any human being could be trusted to handle living salmon day after day without yielding to the temptation to kill and market them. Such folk were aware of the immense profit that could be won, and undoubtedly imagined their own inability to resist such a temptation.

It was about this time that I heard of the arrival in New Brunswick of a fishery scientist from Sweden. Dr Gustave Lindstrom had already spent some time in

Stripping milt from a cock salmon to fertilise the ova taken from the hen. (*Department of Fisheries of Canada*)

The stripping shed and hatchery adjoining a holding pond on a Canadian salmon river. (*Department of Fisheries of Canada*)

Quebec observing the work of spreading the population of 'ouananiche,' the land-locked salmon, among the northern lakes. His visit had been made in order to observe and record Canadian salmon activities, and to search for evidence to help in his quest to discover the secrets of the salmon's ocean feeding ground.

It was with great interest that I first heard over the phone from Headquarters, of the arrival of this celebrated authority on Atlantic salmon, and that Dr Gustave Lindstrom was anxious to visit Camp Musquash to observe the routine at the counting fence. On the following day the Swedish doctor was delivered at the cabin door and the car which had brought him returned.

Between us, a bond of friendship, born of our common interest, sprang up immediately, and I listened with fascination to accounts of research on the rapid rivers of Sweden and Norway, and of his Atlantic salmon three thousand miles away from our present meeting place. Dr Lindstrom listened with great interest to my account of the sixty pounder's journey to notch up a third spawning mark on her scales. He was further impressed when I produced the microscope and one of her scales with the double scar. The fact that he was able to sit in an old cabin fifty miles from the nearest fringe of civilisation and look down a microscope and see by electric light the gathered evidence of a salmon on its way to spawn for the third time, caused him great excitement.

Some days after the doctor's arrival, a cavalcade of four cars descended the hill to Camp Musquash, and I guessed that it was the deputation of inquiry started off by the recent press article. Having had no warning of their intended visit, I assumed that this was an unofficial

Peeping Tom outing which had somehow gained access to the closed road. I turned to the doctor and explained the situation.

'I think you're about to see something of Canadian public opinion, the counting fence isn't exactly popular with the local people, and here's some of them coming down the hill with their war paint on and they'll be whooping round for my scalp I guess.'

Dr Lindstrom had been well briefed over the prejudice of local opinion and he had found it difficult to believe. He looked up from his writing and grinned at me.

'You'll be able to tell them the whole story to change their attitude, eh?' he said by way of encouragement.

The four cars came to a stop outside the cabin and a score of tired-looking New Brunswick men climbed stiffly out. The jolting fifty miles along the Halford dirt road had obviously been more than they had bargained for, they looked hot and tired. Several of them took out packs of cigarettes and proceeded to light up.

One of the party, with the quick skill of a press photographer, took a picture of me as I stood on the verandah wearing my heavily nailed lumber boots, jeans, Scotch plaid shirt, hunting cap and the fringe of black beard about my face.

'I guess you're the guy who's in charge of this salmon trap round here,' he shouted. It was unfortunate that he used the word 'trap' which nettled me at once.

'Then some guy's been pulling your leg, because there's no salmon trap in this district. You're on the wrong river I guess,' I shouted back. 'How did you get in here?' I continued, 'because if you came through the main gate you must have given an understanding that there'd be no smoking in the forest.'

Two of the smokers immediately dropped their cigarettes and trod them in the dust, but the remainder continued to smoke.

'No smokers are allowed in this forest,' I told them, 'if you refuse to put them out you stay here under false pretences, you've got no right to be here.' I turned into the cabin, and a moment later the assembled inquisition who still stood in the hot sunlight outside, heard me asking over the phone for the gatekeeper's number.

'That you Bill?' I shouted, loud enough to be heard outside. 'Got a party of guys here in four cars, did you let 'em in? Half a dozen of 'em are smoking, what shall I do about it?'

The explosive blast that greeted this information was enough to damage my ear-drums, and with the phone held at arms length, I heard the gatekeeper's instruction to get their names. I went outside, but the cigarettes had already followed the first two into the dust. Then I addressed the spokesman, 'Bill Matchett wants a word with you over the phone,' I said, and the language of the one-sided conversation that followed is best not recorded.

'You wouldn't be referring to the Research Salmon Counting Fence when you mentioned the salmon trap, would you?' I asked, after the phone had been put down.

'You call it what you like, son, but we haven't come all this God darned way without intending to see it in action. There's enough public money being spent on this salmon investigation plan, why can't the public be told what they're paying for? What's so secret about this counting fence? Why can't we see it? What have you got to hide.'

I was so astonished at the sudden outburst that I took

a moment to gather my wits together. 'Don't you know,' I retorted, 'that the Fisheries Board has done everything they can to inform the local public on what they propose to do on this river in the next few years? Don't you read your local papers, don't you listen to your radio? I guess there's been enough money and effort spent on trying to inform you guys on our aims at Camp Musquash. There's nothing secret about it, you can see it by all means, so that you'll know what's going on before shouting your mouths off at me.'

I beckoned them over and led them up the well-worn path to where the big triangular frames carried the fence across the river, and sitting on the flat cage roof I told them how the salmon entered the cage at night and how in the morning the wire tags were painlessly inserted into the gristle of the dorsal fin and the fish liberated to continue their journey.

I noticed that Dr Lindstrom had followed the deputation on to the fence. He stood in the background listening as I presented the case for the continuance and even expansion of salmon research in the rivers of the Maritimes.

'There's no doubt about it,' I said, 'that if it were not for the protection and assistance from the Management Programme in our provinces, salmon stocks would be steadily dwindling away. Look at the rivers down in the States, what has pollution, reservoir damming, road-making, and extensive fishing done to their salmon? It's lucky for us that in Canada the danger signal that points towards the extinction of this beautiful fish, has been seen in time. The work of conservation and development of the Federal Department of Fisheries, prevents, detects and corrects pollution in the rivers—and at sea off the estuaries—in order to keep our existing stocks of Atlantic salmon. As New Brunswick men, this is your heritage and one which you should all protect.'

But I got the impression that much of what I said was lost on most of my listeners who seemed to be studying the layout of the fence with a quiet yearning to build a little private one for themselves in some remote trout stream.

I concluded by telling them that they may have found the fifty-mile dirt road a long way to travel, but when compared with the distance which the salmon had swum, their journey was not much. Then to my great surprise Dr Lindstrom began to speak.

'Gentlemen,' began the doctor, 'I have travelled over 3,000 miles to see what is going on in this river. You must not expect your scientists to make a big show of their doings, they are not propagandists who advertise their work like film stars. Their work is usually done quietly and without fuss. Young men like Mr Douglas will be engaged in projects like this, in many parts of your great country, all over the world for that matter, carrying out routine observations and compiling data for enlightenment on some great mystery like the homing power of Atlantic salmon. This fish is an international treasure shared by your country as well as mine, and many other lands. Where do these creatures go in the ocean to feed and grow until they become the most beautiful of all living things? When we learn the secret of the salmon's ocean pastures, we will have uncovered one of the great nature secrets of the world. It's a well-known fact that salmon of these rivers go north as far as the coast of Labrador, and it's a known fact that our fish from Sweden and Norway go north to Iceland, and beyond. It would not surprise me at all if our salmon and your salmon reach the same feeding ground, and that salmon marked by me in Sweden and salmon tagged by our young friend here in the Missimi, may be feeding side by side on the Arctic crustaceans that thrive beneath the ice cap of the regions round the pole. Perhaps that's the gathering ground of all the salmon of the countries round the Atlantic. We may guess and make our theories, but as men of science we must have facts. Some day we'll know the secret of the salmon, which may be given to the world perhaps through the dedicated work done by this young man in the loneliness of this wild and beautiful corner of New Brunswick. I've come all the way from Sweden to see what's going on in this river and I can understand your curiosity gentlemen: once it is satisfied, you will remain to marvel.' The bland smile that accompanied this disclosure, which identified his scholarly quest with their suspicious curiosity, had an extraordinary effect upon the assembled men. Then he continued.

'Two days before I reached here, a salmon went up this river to spawn for the third time. She was nine years old and she weighed sixty pounds. This young man has given me absolute proof of all this. I have it here in my wallet, nature stamps all this information and much more besides, on each scale of the salmon's body and it tells a similar story to the human traveller's passport. Mr Douglas has given me one of her scales, I treasure it, and will take it back with me to Sweden, where it will be enlarged and shown on television. Millions of people will see it and marvel that such a thing should ever come to pass. That is what this boy is doing up here shut off in isolation from his home and friends. He is searching in a quest for *new* knowledge to enrich mankind. You busy people of this great country care little enough about this particular search for truth. Your visit here today suggests a lack of understanding of the high ideals for which this young man stands. A long time ago a crowd went forth to interfere with another young man whose work they did not understand, but that work has lasted for two thousand years.'

The cultured, slightly accented voice of the old world visitor ceased, and in the silence that followed, the limpid gurgle of the river where it fretted through the mesh of the fence, seemed to accentuate the message of the sermon which the visitors had been obliged to listen to. An uneasy shuffling led to a spasmodic clapping which led to a mounting hubbub of conversation as the men argued among themselves. We left them to it, returned to the cabin, and closed the door. What could have been an awkward situation had been successfully averted, and our visitors seemed to be well on the road to conversion.

TEN

THE SANCTUARY OF THE LAKE

Dr Lindstrom remained as my guest for nearly a week, and throughout that time his enquiring mind was rarely idle. Each morning's inspection of the salmon took much longer with his meticulous examination of each fish and the search for marks on the skin and his interpretation of wounds. In this way I learnt to recognise the teeth marks of a grey seal bite, the scars left by lampreys, and the onset of fungus infection.

The presence of sea lice usually near the tail meant that the salmon which carried them had come straight up from the sea, as these parasites soon die in the river. Conversely, the presence of many fresh-water lice on the gills meant that those salmon which carried them had lingered too long in the pools where infestation was heavy. Weal marks made by the meshes of a net indicated a lucky escape at the last moment, a spear jab from above left a vertical mark on the flank, or a cut across the back showed where a trace of hooks had been drawn across the fish in the poacher's hope of catching the barbs in its skin.

There had been occasions in the past when I had wearied of my lonely and monotonous task of marking the fish each morning, but throughout the week in which the Swedish doctor carried out his observations I looked forward each day to the new revelations which he brought to the work, making it a fascinating game of detection. Whether the wounds were old and healed, or fresh and still raw, he invariably seemed to know the cause.

On the day before he was due to leave, I told him the story of the incident with the Boston poachers, and he asked me to show him the long lake. On the following morning we made an early start by canoe, and reached the falls. From there on we followed the ice marks along the river's edge on foot until by midday we came to the peace and beauty of the lake.

The summer heat was over, and already an indefinable touch of autumn had made itself felt in the sighing of the cool wind, the restlessness of the birds, and the ripening of the berries. At one place we decided to leave the lake shore and climb through the bush to a bald hill top for the sake of the view. It was a rough climb and at last we reached the barren rocky summit from where we could see the long lake of Missimi winding for over three miles between the interlacing shoulders of the hills. Between these shoulders many rivers drained the whole great watershed, and over this wild and lonely place the infinite grandeur of arboreal Canada remained untouched by man. Even in the cool depths of the lake the salmon would sense this remoteness from human influence, and we knew that they were enjoying a well-earned rest in its sanctuary and peace.

The calm perfection of the lake was broken by a dark spot that appeared on its surface; it was a bird as big as a goose but with a longer and more streamlined body. It lay in the water rather than on it. It was a great northern diver or loon, a bird which has progressed so far in evolution as a swimmer to catch fast-moving fish, that it can no longer walk or stand on land. We focused our glasses on it.

Then we saw its mate surface a hundred yards away, and the silence of the afternoon was shattered by the cacophony of their yodelling, until the echoes bounded from the sloping forest walls on either side of the lake. Suddenly the two birds glided below the surface and the ripples on the water and the echoes faded behind them and silence returned.

Beneath the water, had we been able to see them, they would have presented a remarkable spectacle of feathered birds swimming and beating the skill and speed of fish in their own element. Unaided by the surprise tactics of the osprey or kingfisher, who strike with the advantage of an aerial dive, the loons flash into action from a standing start, and with incredible swimming power, swerve and circle among the shoals of speckled trout which form their diet. Earlier in the year they had nested on a tiny island at the other end of the lake where two chicks had hatched and taken to the water, but they had been snapped up by an otter, and the two old birds were left to haunt the lake for the remainder of the summer. With the onset of autumn they would return, like the salmon, to spend the winter in the richness of the ocean. In the meanwhile they fished and fed sumptuously on Missimi trout.

Mergansers also lived on the abundant fish life in the lake, and every day each graceful fish duck took from twenty to forty young trout between the saw-toothed edges of its slender beak. Kingfishers and ospreys quartered the shallow inlets and dived whenever a chance presented itself, herons waited in the water, as immobile as tree stumps and from their wide-spread feet a scent was given off which (so the legend goes) attracts the fish until they come within reach of the rapier thrust of the heron's bill. From the feet of herons a secret and illegal preparation is made which (it is claimed) attracts fish to the baited hook of anglers who take advantage of the trick.

We saw a group of rare strangers, the most spectacular of all fisher-birds, eight snow-white gannets from the far off nesting rocks of Bonaventure Island on the coast of Gaspé. To these pelagic wanderers on their six-foot spread of wings, distance meant nothing. Normally they fished at sea, but on rare occasions cruised along river valleys and flew in a long cast over the inland lakes.

We focused our binoculars on them as the skein of eight big birds came over the woodlands from the east flying in line astern, and as they sighted the lake they climbed on stronger wing beats to a height of over a hundred feet. They could see the lines of salmon and the schools of grilse with infinitely clearer vision than our binoculars provided us. Without hesitation each gannet suddenly peeled off and dived straight at the water from a hundred feet. To reduce the shock of hitting the water at such fantastic speed, a system of air sacs has evolved under the skin of the gannets' breasts. These fill with air during the dive and cushion the bird from impact with the water. One after another, eight columns of water flew upwards as the avian bombardment of the salmon took place. After hitting the water, the gannets plummeted on down into the green depths of the lake among the fish. They were as highly specialised for their type of fishing as the loons or the herons were for theirs: ospreys dived hesitatingly feet first into shallow water, the gannets went in like aerial torpedoes, and the first birds to hit the water plummeted straight to their targets and caught a three pound grilse apiece, ten feet below the surface. The great shoal scattered in confusion, and the gannets surfaced, but there was no means of knowing which birds had succeeded for the prey had been quickly swallowed (as they would have done at sea) for if the gannet surfaced with the fish in its beak, it would be robbed by the gulls.

Then they flapped heavily forward on their big wings and were quickly airborne again. But the value of surprise was over, every fish in that part of the lake had felt the stunning impact of the diving birds, and disappeared as though by magic. The big hen salmon had fled in panic and dived in a long slanting line of flight deep into the cold black heart of the lake, where she lay still on the bottom until hours later when the need for companionship sent her swimming in search of her school. The dispersed salmon shoaled up again where the gentle current of the river passed almost imperceptibly through the lake.

Slaughter went on throughout the lake where everything that lived, lived only by the death of others. Between the minute diatoms of plankton and the big hungry trout, life thrived only at the expense of life. As the larvae of midges, gnats and mosquitoes turned into flying insects along the edges of the lake, they were snapped up by trout and salmon parr which swarmed along the shallows at the periods of the hatch.

Over the surface of the lake, we saw huge carnivorous dragon flies flashing iridescent colours in the sunlight. They flew at great speed sometimes suddenly stopping and hovering, turning sharply or flying backwards as they sought their insect prey with their complex bulging eyes that missed nothing. They zigzagged over the reed beds on rustling wings to startle perching insects into flight so that they could catch them in mid-air as a falcon takes its prey. Sometimes a female would pass in graceful dipping flight to touch the water every yard to lay an egg. Some would plant their eggs in slits bitten in hollow stems, later to hatch into nymphs and thrive on the myriad smaller creatures of the underwater world, where life was held so cheap.

Thus the ancient law, kill or be killed, was practised in every cubic inch of the three mile lake, and the only denizens of its murky depths who took no part in killing were the salmon.

Small rafts of duck showed up at times as they gathered on the open water. Golden eye, mallard, widgeon, black duck and canvas backs would become more restless with each day, and gradually their numbers would grow less as they flew eastward to the coast to join the great Atlantic fly way of Canadian ducks that migrate in millions from the Arctic to winter in the south. But the salmon would remain in long shoals on the peat-stained gravelly shillets where the lake narrowed to the river; they also awaited the impetus to move, an urge that would come from the ripening ova within them.

Thus they lay for many days and nights, hardly moving except for the breathing motion of gills and jaws, and the occasional turning fin. Sometimes a member of the shoal would ride mysteriously upwards and forward on a strange transient urge to resume the journey. These individual spurts of enthusiasm awoke no reaction in the others, and the mass of fish continued to lay like sunken pulp logs along the floor of the lake. As the days ran into weeks, fresh contingents of ripening salmon came in from the river, their numbers had already been recorded in the log book at the counting fence and every fish bore its tag of identification. The newcomers crowded in among the earlier fish, and as each fresh contingent came, a wave of restlessness would spread over the first-comers and they would move ever further away from the fresh run salmon. As fish continued to arrive in the dim light of each dawn, earlier shoals, including the giant hen, moved with infinite stealth along the edge of the lake. The gentle shunting forward continued, started anew by the arrival of each dawn contingent. The urgency of the long run up the river now seemed to be over and forgotten, and if the finny denizens of Missimi Lake gave a thought to the great armada of waiting salmon, they must have wondered why they never ate, and hardly moved. But the great Atlantic travellers knew of the coming climax of their lives, they knew why they were there with the sureness of the migrant swallow when it nears the end of its spring migration.

The salmon seemed to sense with instinctive knowledge that when they left the shelter and seclusion of the lake they would be exposed to the glare of sunlight through shallow waters and be at the mercy of predators. In every autumn over countless centuries, salmon had left Missimi Lake to ascend the tumbling cataracts and spawn in the birthplace of both the rivers and the salmon. Throughout that period, Indian hunters of the Micmac and Maliseet tribes had come to spread their nets at the tops of waterfalls into which the salmon had leapt and died in great numbers. Gaffing, spearing and forking went on until the river turned red with blood. The Indian hunters took such a toll that even their dogs could feed on frozen salmon throughout the following winter.

The British and French had come and wrestled for possession of the land. It was given the name of New Brunswick and as the need for paper developed over the world, growing quantities of pulp were needed. The forests of the Indian tribes became of value to the white man, and the red man gradually disappeared from even this ultimate wilderness beyond Missimi Lake.

In the race remembrance of the salmon, the horror of the annual Indian massacres still lingered, as indelibly printed on their minds as the power to recognise the weak scent of the parent river water far out in the Gulf of St Lawrence.

Thus the ever-growing congregation of salmon lay along the edge of the lake from the point where it drained away, to the place where the upper rivers entered. Still they waited on, unable to face the nameless dread of leaving the lake's seclusion to plunge along the stream where so much blood had run.

Now a change was coming over the fish at the head of the queue, most of the dazzling silver which had covered their body scales on leaving the sea had long disappeared. They were returning adults which had gone through the reverse process of when they descended the river as young smolts two and three years before. Then as they swam downstream the spots and dark stripes of the parr stage had gradually disappeared beneath a deposit of silvery guanine. By the time they reached the sea they had become living torpedoes of silver, among the most beautiful of all swimming things. Now as they returned as adults on the reverse route, the river seemed to be reclaiming the silver with which it had decked its baby fish for camouflage in the sea's translucence. The salmon were now turning a dark metallic grey in which the heavy speckle showed more clearly, and dark red spots appeared between the black ones. The stagnant gloom of the lake had added to their steady deterioration, the load of spawn carried by the hens had grown in size, and the curve of their laden bellies sagged heavily. The cocks passed through an even more weird transformation, their nuptual livery assumed a bright red marbled mottling that spread over their bodies from nose to tail and increased in brilliance as the mating time drew near. Their heads showed the greatest change, the upper jaw became curved and elongated which gave it a hideously supercilious appearance, the lower jaw developed a vertical kype that stood upright at the tip at right angles to the waxy gums. The purpose of the kype was to enable the wearer to grip and hold a rival cockfish by the tail and swim against the current when his victim would be partly drowned. Thus arrayed, the gallant males started to conduct their sallies along the ranks of the hitherto indifferent hens. As time passed aggression developed, the males grew more dominant, and fights and wrestling bouts began. The hens were unconcerned with this growing male activity, and even when a pair of males would lock their curving jaws together and wrestle and shake like fighting terriers, until the surrounding water became discoloured, the hens continued to ignore them except to move away from the brawling scene.

The temperature of the lake fell slowly, storms of rain swept over the mountains and discoloured water spread into the lake from every stream and river in the watershed. These murky distillations of autumn reached the salmon where they lay around the spruce-clad islands at the lake's head. As the first faint whisps of a forest fire start the woodland creatures off in flight, so these first whisps of discoloured water stirred the dormant salmon into motion. Then as the gloom of approaching night spread over the lake they began moving forward in the freshening elixir of the taste of flood. At last their time had come, and they nosed their way among the rocks and labyrinth of long dead sunken logs and debris that the storms of centuries had washed down from the forests: the autumn spawning run was on.

As the big hen rose to take her place in the lines of moving fish, a dull red cock fish shadowed her, for several weeks the two had never been far apart, whenever she had shifted her position he too had moved like a long red shadow to hover always near at hand. There had been no sign of recognition from her, indeed the only sign of interest which he had shown in her was when other cock fish came too close.

Side by side or one behind the other they continued to nose between the boulders. There were big hens and tiny males, and little hens accompanied by monstrous cock fish whose long curved snouts and cadaverous jaws seemed more calculated to terrify male rivals than to win the hearts of chosen females. Thus decked in the colourful glory of their nuptial livery of mottled red, the nomads of the ocean began to take their places for the start of the final phase of the grand migration to the mountains.

ELEVEN

SEXUAL FANTASY

The river was considerably smaller where it entered the head of the lake than at the point where it flowed away. As the salmon filed nervously into the narrow river's mouth to begin the most hazardous part of the journey, they could hear the rumbling tumult of its passage from the hills. To the homing migrants, now well rested after their long wait in the lake, the taste and sound of the birth river unleased emotions of intense excitement.

Twice before, the big hen had lingered in the lake until the urge within her could no longer be constrained. Now stimulated by the presence of her attendant male, she ploughed for a third time into the blinding froth bubbles and eddying clouds of fallen leaves, and yielded herself to the joyous thrill in the currents and cataracts that thundered from the autumn tinted woods. The scent of fallen leaves was strong in the water again, arboreal confetti for the wedding of the salmon. For her the dread fears of the previous months were disappearing in the drugged delirium of her happiness in reaching her natal stream: the vivid sense of danger which had saved her for so long was blunted. Vaguely she remembered the white maelstrom as she nosed in over the clean river-washed stones on the bed of the pool, then acting on a sudden impulse she thruddled upwards through the canopy of bubbling whiteness and out and up into the crisp autumn air to cleave the smooth brow of the waterfall with a solid thump, and disappear among the rocks beyond. Other salmon followed her, some succeeded but many were swept back to try again and again. Meanwhile the great hen fish climbed on through the twisting currents of the singing river, and the enrichening oxygen of the bubbling water gave her added strength. But her spawn load had grown so heavy during the sojourn in the lake that after a mile of cataracts and waterfalls she came to rest between some granite boulders with her dorsal fin awash.

She remained in the shelter of the big stones in a state of careless excitement and only rarely felt a fleeting tinge of fear. Her camouflage had been changed by the six weeks' stay in the dark lake, and her back was almost black, shading off through tones of mottled pewter grey to a russet gold liberally spotted with red and black. Until this deep-lake camouflage changed, she was ill-equipped to linger in the shallows where a passing eagle would have seen her from above. In the ever-growing coldness of the water the first taste of the acid tang of muskeg peat came to her mingled with alder roots and balsam. She beat her tail and moved on, soon she would reach the chosen place of burial for her life's treasure, the redd beneath the alder muskeg. There the great cock salmon would be waiting for her as their ancestors had been waiting every autumn for countless millions of years. Both cock and hens would obey the laws of nature that prompted them to act when the time was ripe. For the old hen, her time was fast approaching as she tailed her way majestically against the ever-dwindling current.

Gradually she sensed that she was nearing her journey's end. The scent from the alders of the muskeg released a soothing flood of satisfaction that heralded the end of her epic swim-way. She beat her tail more vigorously and glided over some sloping shillets of fine gravel and sank into a clear pool where she spread her pectorals and rested on the stones.

Her passage through the shallows had not gone unobserved, she would have been the last to notice it, but her allure for the males of her species attracted cock salmon parr no larger than three inches in length who quarrelled frantically among themselves for the honour of fertilising the spawn of the mighty hen who towered above them.

The endless gurgling water music that sang over the clean stones of the river bed, lulled the tired hen into a restful trance where past memories mingled with the bliss of the coming climax of her life. Soon she would shed her load of spawn, her debt to posterity would be paid, and she could then yield to the long ride back to her ocean home, unless the ice jaws of an early winter closed over the redds and held her pool bound until the spring.

The deep and clear rock pool where she passed the day, was one of a great many such pools; they were separated by small waterfalls where the river dropped as though by steps. The V-shaped glen was a riot of autumn colours and the stands of hardwood, oak, and maple stood out in their individual blazing tints that glowed from the palest yellow of the larch and poplar to the brightest maple red, and between them stood the dense green of the conifers.

This was the rutting season of the Moose, and throughout the day the steep glens echoed to the grunting coughs of the bulls, who stood seven feet in height as they roamed the forest questing for a partner or another male to fight. Then over the snorting of the bulls came a fresh sound, as long skeins of Canada geese passed high across the forested hills in a series of wavering pennants and their haunting bugle notes floated down and told the world beneath them that *Glooscap*, the snow God, was on his way. The orderly V-shaped squadrons passed across the sky and the honking and trumpeting faded away towards the south, and the valley was left to the grunting mating calls of the moose, the crashing of the rivers and the cold rising wind in the swaying branches of the trees, as the first foretaste of approaching winter followed in the wake of the geese.

This was the mating time of the deer and the salmon, in both the mammals and the fish many months must pass before the unborn young developed in readiness for birth. When the moose calf is born the sap is rising, and sprouting vegetation is at its best for the growing calf or fawn, and lactation in the mother is at its richest. Similarly for the hatching salmon fry whose emergence from the egg coincides with the explosive growth of plankton and the gradual hatching of insects, crane flies, stone flies, caddises, midges and may flies. The fry grow rapidly into the little striped parr who feed savagely on each successive hatch of insects throughout the summer, until by the autumn they reach four or five inches in length.

The big hen's passage from the lake had been remarkable for one strange feature, the irresistible attraction that she held for some of the tiny male salmon parr who sensed her movement through the water.

In all the world of nature there is no stranger fantasy of sex than this ambitious love of the parr for the adult female salmon as she prepares to spawn. Naturalists, fishermen, and wardens have seen it, photographers have filmed it, scientists have sought a reason for it, and poachers have laughed at it. But it has been proved that the sperm potential from this tiny mite is capable of fertilising a clutch of spawn fifty times its total weight. This phenomenon of the parr's devotion towards his gargantuan mistress is one of the most interesting facets in the whole amazing courtship of the salmon.

Everywhere along her journey up the final river, tiny salmon felt the urge to follow in obedience to the sex lure which she left behind her. But with the fading of her scent the small fish returned to normal and food watching stations were resumed once more.

In the rock pool where the big hen settled, the male parr were immediately attracted to her side, the biggest kept the others away with murderous attacks until a bigger one arrived to depose him. This game of king of the castle went on until the biggest parr in the pool, whose length from nose to tail extended for four inches and whose weight was slightly more than an ounce, mounted guard over his sixty pound mistress. He was, in fact, capable of fertilising the whole twenty pounds of spawn carried by the hen.

He lay beside her in the cold October water oblivious of everything, even passing morsels of food, for from her came the scent of ripening spawn.

Surely this is the most fantastic precaution against

infertility in the adult male to be found anywhere in nature. It is an insurance worthy of the supreme risk taken by hen salmon in their colossal journeys from the Atlantic to the mountain streams of Canada, Britain, Scandinavia and all the other spawning rivers that border the ocean. In all these breeding grounds of salmon, the tiny sperm-charged parr lie waiting in the currents ready to assist in the procreation of their kind.

Suddenly the shadow of a passing deer fell over the pool, and as it crossed the salmon, the little parr felt the stunning turbulence as she beat her tail and disappeared into the shallows like a dark torpedo, leaving her tiny amourata to regain his physical balance and lament her passing.

As the questing hen fish reached another pool she sank slowly down and came to rest on extended fins behind four grilse who had spent the day in its seclusion. A little covey of quarrelsome male parr were threatening each other's extermination over the possession of the female grilse who remained oblivious of even the presence of the tiny cavaliers. The sudden arrival of a new hen caused fresh consternation, and the fact that the newcomer was twenty times the weight of the grilse was of little importance, if anything her attraction for them was stronger than the grilse, and she became the centre of a furious battleground of thrust and counter thrust as over her back and round her tail and to and fro beneath her belly, the little salmon of the river fought until the smaller ones were driven off and obliged to fall back and seek consolation in the company of the grilse who were merely forty times their weight.

With the coming of darkness the big hen suddenly shot past the young salmon, and struggled up through the flurry of a shallow cataract with her richly spotted back and dorsal fin clear of the water. As long as she could keep her head and gills from the air and feel the comforting resistance of the water against the thrust of her tail, she was content to struggle on and on.

Before she could settle down to spawn, several things were needed; the suitable environment of the right size gravel, the speed of the current, and the all important stimulus of the shivering nearness of a cock fish. Her mate had been left far behind at the high falls, and only if he succeeded in leaping the obstacle could he share her redd. The natural obstacles in the swim-ways of the salmon ensured that only the finest of these great fish could reach the best spawning water near the source of Missimi. It was the offspring from such parents who had the strength to reach the mountains, that stood the best chance of survival in the early stages of life. High up on the plateau where the river was born, hungry trout and eels were few, the water was rich in oxygen, and parr food was plentiful. Such a place was the ultimate goal of the giant hen, and only death would prevent her from reaching it.

TWELVE

COURTSHIP UNDER THE ICE

That night as she nosed her way stealthily through the shallows from one pool to the next, she was at times half out of the water, and it was always a relief to sink into the safety of a pool.

For two miles she struggled from one pool through shallow rapids to the next, higher and ever higher, where only a small number of salmon would be able to join her. But they would come as they had always come, the élite of the multitudes which had waited in 'million dollar pool.' The determined hens would climb with the last ounce of their strength and courage to bear their precious eggs to the safety of the mountain rivulets.

At last the long succession of tumbling rapids ceased, and the huge grey salmon lay gasping under the shadow of the alder bushes that overhung the stream. Daylight had come and she was content to lie hidden from danger in the quiet peace of the water. She scented the presence of other salmon further ahead, as the current brought the familiar rancid scent of ripening hens, and with it came the longing for the presence of her big red mate, who had failed at the seven-foot jump. In the days when he had shadowed her everywhere among the dying weeds of the lake, she had taken his presence for granted, now she waited with expectant longing for his arrival, for without the stimulus of his presence she would be unable to shed her mass of ova.

Some hours later a tired cock and hen passed quietly on their way to the redds, and they were shadowed at a respectful distance by a smaller cock fish in poor condition, slight patches of fungus were already spreading over parts of his head and neck. As he saw the grey leviathan in the alder shadows he swung round and came to rest beside her. He was tired and hideously ugly, a mere caricature of the noble cock fish he had been when he left the head of tide and started on this cruel journey. For some time the two fish lay side by side, the big hen enjoyed the fact of his companionship, and he the tantalising bliss of the presence of an unattached female.

All night the two fish lay resting near the alder, occasionally the hen would draw away from the hook-nosed cock, but he was now more rested and wherever she moved he gently followed behind her.

As the grey November dawn spread over the eastern hills, the light revealed a moorland about half a mile in width and surrounded on three sides by hills. This was the end of the journey.

On the threshold of winter the wide moor was a grim forbidding place of dying grass and Sphagnum moss, sparsely peppered with stunted conifers and long-dead, bleached and withered skeletons of standing tree trunks, remnants of a forest fire of long ago. Everywhere the countless rivers of the bog seeped lisping from the cradle of the moor, and where they met and merged, the great Missimi started on its journey to the sea. Thus fed, the river meandered through the muskeg over clean wide belts of gravel which made perfect burying places for the spawn of salmon.

Throughout the autumn this place had echoed to the ringing calls of feeding waders on migration from the Arctic to the pampas. Long skeins of bugling geese had planed down, rested and gone. For the wedges of wild duck, mallard, teal, canvas back and golden eye, on the New Brunswick flyway between Labrador and the coast of Maine, it had been an open oasis in the endless forests, a refuge where no gun fired. For the waders and plovers that flew by the land route to Patagonia it was the final feeding ground before crossing high over the United States border to follow the coast route to the winter feeding grounds of the Orinoco, the Matto Grosso or the Pampas of the Argentine. Its wide emptiness meant inviting safety to these aerial nomads of the sky and whatever the appetites of the waterfowl the great muskeg could cater for it: the crowberry crop for the birds and the teeming insect life that fed the salmon fry whose parents had made the climb.

A family of five mergansers which had been reared entirely on young salmon from spring until the fall, together with their parents, had each consumed at the rate of thirty tiny fish per day, depleting the salmon nurseries by about twelve thousand parr and smolts, before the voices of the passing waterfowl attracted them to begin the break up of the family and start their own migration southward. This apparent havoc wrought by mergansers among young fish throughout the summer should be considered against the fact that such crowded summer feeding grounds would be unable to support the vast hatch in the confines of the narrow stream, the intervention of the birds adjusted the balance.

If only a limited number of salmon could reach this place, fewer still would escape from it. For the hens there was a chance of safety if they spawned quickly and dropped back to the shelter of the deep lake. But for the cocks who lingered too long in the shallows awaiting the arrival of more hens, the closing jaws of ice would bring certain death.

For several weeks before the coming of the salmon, the trilling, bugling, piping, quacking and whistling of the migrants had brought music to the high moor, but the last late wandering curlews and whimbrel, flying southward from the Arctic had stayed only a little while. Early one morning they had risen piping contentedly to each other and climbed steadily towards the south-west.

A tall bull moose trotted over the muskeg; the great spread of his palmated antlers swayed as he moved, symbolising the grandeur of wild Canada, he paused several times to look uneasily about him before disappearing into the birch scrub where the gathered water of Missimi started its plunging course into the valley. Then the dying moor was left to the salmon and the silent cruel splendour of approaching winter.

All sign of life had gone except where fourteen fish lay in a wind-ruffled stretch of open water. Six of them were hens and beside each one a cock fish lay restless and watchful, for the remaining two unmated salmon gave them little peace. For over two hundred miles these males had swum the gauntlet of the dangers of the river and made the final grand ascent to its source to claim a worthy bride. This was the *ultima Thule*, which only the élite members of the countless hosts could attain through the limit of determination and strength. But, even so, there were two males too many.

The six mating couples occupied a stretch of gravel as far from each other as was possible, and as either of the two cock salmon approached a mated pair, he would expose himself to the savagery of an attack from the other males. But most of the defending males were content with a vigorous dismissal of the intruder and a speedy return to the waiting hen. They were probably aware that if she was left unguarded, another would be likely to establish a claim to her in the absence of the rightful lord. Fights perhaps on that account were more in the nature of displays of savagery which resulted in strategic withdrawals by the invaders so that advances could be made from the other side. Several times cock salmon tried to grip each other about the head and snouts, and on one occasion a fish was gripped round the base of the tail and the kype was used to its best advantage. The grip was perfect and the fish promptly turned and swam upstream dragging his victim by the tail backwards against the current; it would have drowned him had he not been able to grip his antagonist by the tail to prevent further progress upstream. They whirled furiously like savage dogs, and then the incredible happened. The cocks released their tail grip and closed again jaw on jaw, each salmon gripped and locked and a bulldog struggle of sheer strength took place.

The flashing commotion in the stream attracted the attention of an observer whose vision missed nothing. It was a white-headed, white-tailed bald eagle who drifted effortlessly southward beneath the misty ceiling of the clouds. Sighting the movement of the fish, his circling ceased and he went into a long flexed glide in the direction of the muskeg.

Far below, the battle of the cock fish raged with unabated fury, this was no ordinary token struggle over a mate. The two salmon had gripped with their curved jaws in such a way that neither could release himself from his opponent. Both fish struggled in a paroxysm of terror and fury, with fin rays extended and big tails lashing from side to side as they churned the shallow water into frothy patterns. A lingering torment would be their fate until the great freeze-up would come to relieve them of their lives, but nature had other plans for the expendable males. The descending speck in the sky dropped ever lower over the circling hills, and the river veined muskeg rushed up to meet him.

The two salmon lay in shallow water, gasping in their lock of death as they awaited a revival of strength to resume the struggle. The huge bird passed over, lowered its yellow legs and sunk its talons into one of the fish. The weight was twice as great as it had expected. Fifty yards was as far as the eagle could struggle before the weight of the two salmon, still locked like ferrets, brought it down among the rocks, where the great bird gorged itself on fish that had proved themselves worthy of a better fate.

In the river there was harmony at last and the giant hen fish sensed the quietness and peace. Her consort lay beside her in the clear singing current and behind them a flotilla of little parr, tails waving and their wonderful eyes as watchful for passing morsels of food, as they were for the first signs of spawning in the big hen. The hook-jawed male moved to and fro and each time he approached his mate he shivered violently from head to tail. These were the first steps in the final stages of salmon courtship. Without this stimulus from the male, which was the outward sign of his fertility, she could not be induced to shed her spawn. Each instinctive act in the interplay of courtship, was needed to stimulate the next step which led to the shedding of the spawn. At last she turned over on her side and started to dig a depression in the gravel which would receive the first batch of ova. For some seconds she lay on her side vigorously beating her tail, and the powerful updraft made by the fanning tail stirred up the stones and gravel, and the strength of the current carried them away. In the hollow thus formed, she rested, as a nest-building hen bird rests in the hollow of her nest.

This action is normally referred to as 'cutting' but to those who have watched it more closely it may be more accurately described as winnowing, the sudden upthrust of the tail sucks the stones up with it and the current washes them away, and a hollow is formed.

The red cock watched the great grey speckled barrel of his partner's body curve sinuously into the first slight depression in the stones, and his excitement mounted. His hooked snout, upcurved lower jaw and twisted gums worked steadily as he kept position. He resembled a hideous old witch keeping guard over a magic brew. But there was far more magic in the plain unvarnished fact of salmon courtship and migration than in the most fantastic flights of man invented witchcraft.

On a sudden impulse he moved forward again and shivered violently from head to tail; the shiver was repeated several times, then the great hen left her stony couch and started winnowing once more. The gravel was fanned into a cloud and the current washed it on again and the hollow deepened.

The cock did nothing to help, he merely awaited the climactic moment when the first stream of ova would be laid in the redd. Then he would be stimulated to fertilise the eggs.

In the world outside the water, the air was growing steadily colder, and in the rising wind that swept in gusts across the empty muskeg was the hint of coming storms. All traces of the gaiety of the early fall had faded from the forest, and the unremitting sadness of winter's sterile grasp was closing over the dying windburnt land. The turbulent and swollen rivers thundered and boomed as they blundered like blinded giants escaping from the prison walls of the valleys, and as Missimi lashed its way towards the freedom of the sea it took with it the first hen salmon which had spawned early in the tributaries of the lake. Their return to the ocean was already under way.

Camp Musquash, in its sheltered glen, was a very different spectacle from the summer idyll. I had helped to dismantle the counting fence and the heavy timbers and mesh had been stacked behind the huts above the level of spring floods. Doors had been locked and windows battened down.

My full report on the season's work at the counting fence had been submitted at the end of September. It aroused much interest at Provincial and Federal Headquarters, and it was decided to send in a small party by air to Lake Missimi to examine and report on conditions at the upper spawning grounds. To my great joy I was invited to join the expedition.

It was a bleak morning in early November when I reported at the fishery office in Saint John harbour where in company with two scientific officers we boarded the aircraft and took off over the water of the Saint John River estuary, patterned by masses of foam from the famous Reversing Falls. We climbed northward and flew over the interminable forest for nearly an hour, and the noise and intense cold were not conducive to conversation. Eagerly I scanned the grey wilderness below for the first sign of my beloved river, and at last my vigil was rewarded as the long dark waterway of the lake resolved itself in the distance. Gradually the plane was brought lower to make a circuit of the place selected by the pilot for landing. At last he was satisfied that his chosen patch of water was free of half-submerged branches, and he lowered the plane gently on to the lake and taxied past the islands to where the main rivers entered. By the time all the gear was put ashore in the inflatable rubber dinghy, the afternoon was far advanced and the pilot took off down the lake, having promised to return in three days time.

When the drone of the engines faded into the distance we turned to the basic necessities of all such expeditions, comfort and warmth. The tent was erected in a clearing beside the lake, air mattresses were inflated, a quantity of firewood was gathered and a good blaze started for preparing the evening meal. Then by the light of a swinging lantern we made our plans for the following day as the darkness of the early winter night came over the scene. My two friends turned into their sleeping bags and I picked up the little rifle and walked into the darkness along the lake shore. The going was much easier than it had been at the height of summer for the rich grass and undergrowth had died back. I walked on into the gusty night with the crashing of wind-swung branches overhead and the splashing of the lake waves at my feet.

In the distance I could hear the rumbling of one of the three main rivers where it crashed towards the lake, and when I reached it and saw and heard the spectacle of its headlong entry into the lake from the sloping forest glen, I marvelled and wondered at the prospect of salmon ascending such a place. I remained there for some time in the darkness and the cold damp spindrift, happy to be within the sound of salmon water, until the falling temperature drove me back to camp.

After breakfast on the following morning, we prepared for the day. Clad in warm clothes and waders we left camp and reached our chosen rivers which we were to follow until we reached the spawning ground.

For two hours I climbed steadily through the trackless forest until at last I was rewarded by spectacular glimpses through the trees of the watershed about the head of the long lake that zigzagged into the distance below me.

Gradually the waterfalls grew smaller, and the runs between them grew calmer and longer. In every stretch of easy water, salmon lay in pairs, the hens 'cutting' and the red males keeping watch and ward over their industrious partners. Occasionally fights and scuffles broke out where unmated cock fish tried to interfere with mated fish. In the clear water, I could see every salmon, and kept a careful count of the numbers as the rough miles went slowly by, and nearly every speckled back that broke the surface bore my tag. A steeper series of difficult waterfalls led up through a final cutting in the rocks and gave out on to a level muskeg plain sheltered on three sides by small hills.

I assured myself that no salmon could come this far

and there seemed little point in following the winding level stretches through the bog, but prompted by an urge to look over the hills beyond, I walked on beside the dwindling river. To my amazement I passed five pairs of spawning salmon, and then on rounding a tussocky bend, I saw the big grey speckled back and triangular dorsal fin of my sixty-pounder standing out of the shallow water. Very slowly I sank to the ground, then crept forward, easing my binoculars in front until I reached the edge of the bank. With great care I brought my eyes to the lenses and focused on the black spots and stiff rays of the fin. Out of pure academic interest I read the number on the tag, but of course I knew that no other fish approaching her size had passed through my hands. Even without the final confirmation of the tag number, I knew that she was the sixty pounder which I had first seen in 'million dollar pool,' and later at the counting fence when I had removed the fly hooks from her jaws, and again at the leaping place. She had reached the end of her journey and was preparing to pour out the seed of her charmed life into the gravel. I felt a deep sense of gratitude to the providence which had enabled me to meet up with her at four stages in her epic journey.

I looked along the dark length of her leaden grey flanks on which a maze of rust red spots and blotches showed, but the perfect symmetry of her streamlined shape had gone. Her back was straighter and thinner, and her belly sagged enormously. Beside her lay the cock fish less than one-third her size, glowing a dull red from nose to tail and over his head three spreading patches of whitish fungus were clearly visible.

I laid the binoculars aside and put on my polaroid glasses to reduce the effect of light on the water, and make the fish more clearly visible. In this way I lay for several hours watching the gradual emergence of the courtship ritual of the salmon. Time after time the cock fish gave his shiver, and occasionally the hen turned on to her side and winnowed the gravel with her tail, and after each operation the hole grew deeper until it seemed about twelve inches in depth. Between each spasm of winnowing the old fish settled deeper into her hollow in the gravel. It seemed an age before I saw her open her mouth as though about to give a yawn which signalled the laying of the first batch of eggs. The cock fish saw the movement and dropped into the hollow beside his giant mistress, who started to pour her brilliant red orange seed into the comparatively still water at the base of the redd, and as she did so the water round the eggs turned slightly milky as the cock fish fertilised them with his creamy milt. But quick though he was to respond to the signal from his mate, another male was quicker, a little ripe parr three inches in length had been lurking between the big stones at the bottom of the redd directly beneath the giant hen, and her spawn came pouring about him as a mass of balloons released from above float down on the heads of dancers, and his milt was extruded even before that of his mighty rival.

The big cock salmon swam quietly away and the hen moved out of the redd and settled short of a yard above her trench where she turned on her side and started tail-winnowing again. Once more the stones and gravel were stirred into suspension and washed downstream to settle in the excavated trench where they automatically covered up the fertilised ova. Time after time the old hen turned over and winnowed the gravel and the current continued to wash it down. By the time she was satisfied that the second trench was sufficiently deep and wide, the excavated debris had been washed down into the first hole and the spawn lay buried beneath a covering of ten inches of gravel, and was safe for the winter. This was the first of many such excavations that she would have to make before the whole of her precious load would be safely buried.

I crawled backwards to avoid disturbing her, and climbed stiffly to my feet, the bitter wind sang over the muskeg and I was cramped with the cold, and it took some vigorous trotting to restore normal warmth. But as I made my way down into the darkening forest beside the river I felt a glow of satisfaction at having been able to see the culminating stage in the journey of the salmon of which I knew so much.

On the following morning we were wakened by an ominous whispering from the lake, the temperature had fallen considerably. Throughout the night thin ice had formed over it but the continuous action of the wind on the water had broken and washed the ice into the bays and inlets near the camp where it was piled into a carpet of floating fragments that rustled and tinkled with the movement of the waves.

After breakfast we set off for a last examination of the spawning. I returned by the same route to the high moor. The wind had increased, which made observation more difficult. Everywhere along the calmer stretches of the muskeg river, the ice had formed from bank to bank except where the six pairs of salmon still worked, the movements of the spawning fish continually broke the surface and prevented ice from forming. Where the big hen was still 'cutting,' and for a distance of several yards below her, the area of stones that marked the redd was clear of the dark peaty stain that covered the surrounding river bed. At the top end of the clean strip of shingle the great fish lay gasping with mouth wide open as she made her final efforts at spawn extrusion accompanied and encouraged by the male. Her grey flanks had collapsed, her stomach had shrunk and she looked a mere shadow of her previous magnificence. She had lost about one-third of her body weight of spawn. Now a cavity lay between her limp flanks, and she must have felt that her life was over. Even as I stood there watching, she started to drop back. With a listless attitude, the long limp shape of the fish seemed to renounce all further struggle with the current, and slightly curved, she allowed herself to be carried down over the length of clean gravel in which she had left between forty and fifty thousand potential salmon. As she came to the lower end of her redd she gave a feeble movement of the tail as though reluctant to be swept away from the place which she had swum so far to reach, but the final ounce of her great strength had obviously gone, and the young Missimi carried the spent old kelt away beneath its thin veneer of ice, and she yielded to the current with a great infinity of sadness. Once or twice she gave a tired flutter of the tail as though to return to her sacred patch, but the current, like a firm nurse with a patient at the limit of its weakness, hurried her away.

Perhaps the spirits of the great Canadian wild had marked her out for special protection and were determined to see her safely back to the deep lake for the winter after all that she had done for her kind. As the current gathered speed, she was carried along the curving river's course across the muskeg. I walked along the bank and purposefully kept on the upper side of her to keep her going downstream, for if she found the strength to return and linger for some days the ice doors would be locked for the winter and she would never escape. When at last I saw her riding tail first into the current by which the river started its series of little cataracts and waterfalls down to the lake, I knew that she would not have the strength to return to her redd, this would be my last view of her.

In the immediate years to come I would be waiting for her at the counting fence again, but in my heart I felt that the chance of her surviving for a fourth spawning run was very remote. As I watched her disappear tail first into the growing current I knew that it was good-bye.

For me the expedition was over, and I hurried back to camp under an ever-darkening curtain of cloud. I was first at the tent and soon had a roaring fire to welcome my two companions.

On the following morning there was no jingling music from dancing fragments of ice at the edges of the lake, only the silence of frozen water round the lakeside and the mantling of winter's first fall of snow. At midday the plane arrived and we made our escape over the freezing water, and as we climbed above the forest I took a last look at the grey lake winding among the whitening hills and wondered if the giant kelt had reached its safety.

THIRTEEN

THE CALL OF THE OCEAN

The big hen salmon seemed to realise that to linger in the freezing river was dangerous, it may have been the presence of the forming ice that frightened her, or the sharp fall in temperature was too unpleasant in her emaciated condition, but she gave way easily before the current which carried her down. In some of the pools where her progress came to a standstill she found other spent hens like herself, and she rested beside them, and a strange lassitude would steal over her, but with it would come a longing for peace in a quieter place than such crowded pools afforded. One by one the spent hens would yield to the current and allow themselves to be drawn tail first into the rapids or over the waterfalls back, back, back. It was easy, always so easy to give in to the masterful strength of the lusty growing river for somewhere at the other end, rest and food and the great revival of strength, spirits, and dynamic courage was waiting to be welded once more into their wasted frames.

Throughout the darkness of the night, the spent fish were taken back down into the forest on the first stage of their long return. The first snow fell and was gathered into floating slushy rafts in sheltered places, snow water was hateful to the salmon and they slipped back, sometimes queueing nose to tail in narrow places, hens only. The cocks remained near the redds fighting over unmated late arrivals, as they would continue to do until it would be too late and the ice would prevent any further descent. Up in the high places they would now be frozen in and held until the spring when famished carrion-hunting foxes would find them still preserved at the break up of the ice. Mortality among the males was always high; their enthusiasm for fertilising spawn usually brought about their end, and even among the great numbers which avoided fixation in the ice, they became so wasted at the redds that their chances of reaching the sea and returning again were remote.

The big kelt felt herself sliding over the curve of the seven-foot waterfall and down into the seething cauldron below, and shortly afterwards the movement of the water slowed and the familiar scent of the lake returned again, the dark quiet peace had been reached, here was her winter sanctuary.

As the days ran on into weeks the surface of the lake became covered with an ever-thickening layer of ice over which the snow fell and in the water beneath, everything was in darkness. For the salmon it was a period of semi-hibernation when their tired and wasted frames lay in a state of relaxation at the bottom of the lake. They seldom moved in the icy darkness, and a change came over them once more as the pigment of their scales turned dark under the influence of the gloom in which they spent the winter months.

As spring returned to the eastern highlands and the temperature rose sharply, the snow fields melted and the rivers rose to their highest level, but the giant kelts still lay like drunken sleepers at the bottom of the lake.

Gradually the foretaste of flood-coloured water made them stir uneasily and their yearning for the ocean was revived as they felt the coming fulfilment in the earth scent of the water. A dreamy restlessness spread over them as the approaching flood began to cloud the lake. One after another they rose in answer to the summons in the water and started patrolling in little groups and schools. The dead and almost dead lay festered with fungus unable to rise until death relieved them of their misery. The others awakened to a long-forgotten sense of hunger, felt the returning urge to kill and eat, but they were still too weak from the torpor of the winter's fast. Fortunately for them they were unable to gratify their early hunger pangs. In common with all creatures after hibernation, the desire to gorge must not be gratified, for death would follow. Suitable food for the salmon was scarce, and they lacked sufficient strength to chase the speckled trout that tantalised them everywhere.

Within the space of a week, the ice that covered the lake was broken into millions of fragments, and gradually at first the floating pieces moved towards the spillway at the eastern end. The stately convergence of the floes ended in a jostling ice jam where the river left the lake; rafts of ice were pushed together by the irresistible pressure from behind; they were piled up and twisted on end, some were ground into powder snow against the rocks and others were gradually lifted as the build up went on until great quantities went sliding on to the surrounding river bank. Under this gigantic flotsam of the dying winter, the muddy water of the flood roared like an express train. For three days this movement of the ice went on in a mad cacophony of thunder, along the gorge and over the falls, blundering and bashing its way until it reached the quiet of the calm flats where it moved more steadily, taking the wide turns in a slow majestic grandeur of movement, each ice floe shrinking as it melted slowly towards the sea.

The salmon were not slow to follow the ice out of the lake and along the opened river. By day and night the dark kelts started dropping back, the giant hen among them, and in the fast-flowing water she felt the great renaissance of life beginning all over again as she started for a fourth time towards the distant sea.

As the turbid water cleared and daylight reached the mending fish they were seen to have changed colour since the fall. The hideous nuptial masks which the cock fish had assumed for the mating period had gone, the jaws had almost returned to normal, the red colour of the body had disappeared. The cocks and hens were difficult to distinguish from each other, and they were all dark in colour after their long wait in the inky depths. But there was one exception, a light brown fish which had gone blind in the previous summer. When all her companions were light in colour, her sight had gone, and lacking the visual stimulus, the pigment in her skin could not now be changed. The blind fish had no need of food in the river, and the sensitive nerve-endings in her lateral line presented a clear picture of surrounding obstacles, and so she had been able to keep within the swimming vibrations of her fellows and follow them towards the sea.

The toughest fishermen who could face the savage cold, had overhauled their tackle and, wrapped up in warm clothing, were afloat once more in their long canoes, flogging the heavy water with their backs to the wind as the black salmon moved down towards the sea.

Another year had started and the season had opened. The fishery laws of New Brunswick permitted the taking of black salmon which had spawned and survived the winter. The fish were hungry and took more readily to the artificial lures, fly, minnow, or bunch of worms depending on the condition of the water.

As they continued to drop back the magical process of preparation for life in the sea took place again as it had done when they descended as smolts. Over every scale on the bodies of the survivors, a deposit of silvery guanine was laid, and as they journeyed down feeding frugally on the slowly emerging insect life, their shrunken stomachs started working again to extract nourishment from worms, flies, grubs and any bits of moving life that caught their eye. If they had been obliged to feed in the rivers as they feed at sea, their journey to spawn would have ended in starvation long before they could reach the spawning grounds, as no river could support them. But now this gradual feeding prepared their stomachs for the banquets of the sea. The big hen regained her marine livery, and armoured once more in this silvery splendour, she grew impatient of the slow procession. She turned suddenly in a flashing curve to face the way ahead, and as she turned, the sunlight caught the great expanse of her silvered broadside, an angler saw it and gasped with disbelief, he passed the word along, and eventually the story reached my ears that a mighty salmon of fabulous proportions had been seen with a school of kelts on its way down river. It was the great one I had known, she had made it once again, and I was filled with happiness at the knowledge that she was going home to grow once more perhaps into still greater splendour.

As the river's tempo slowed, the big hen and the gleaming school of mended kelts kept on towards the head of tide through deep and quiet pools and ever-widening stretches, under bridges and rafts of floating logs, for the great pulp drive had started. At last they reached the darkness of nearly half a mile of floating timber, held back by the snubber boom above the noisy mill. Onward they swam, a mere remnant of the mighty host which had migrated inland in the previous year. Those that had survived the winter in the lake had steadily dwindled in the rough and tumble of the roaring spate as they were bowled along in the wake of the ice. Many had been taken by anglers and still greater numbers had been netted out by poachers. Thus the remaining band of survivors followed in the wake of the old hen's tail vibrations, they swam blind for the moving water kept the thick foul ooze of mud in suspension before them and they moved into an ever-darkening world of brown oblivion. Through the acrid stench of chemical effluent from the pulp mill, the sewage of towns and the complex tainted streams of road tar, oil, D.D.T., minerals, household refuse and detergents. It seemed as though humanity was bent on stopping the kelts from going out, but through everything came the strong compelling call of the sea.

Southward for six hundred miles along the coast, the rivers of the U.S.A. had always given breeding sanctuary to the salmon of the Atlantic, but as industry and human population grew, the rivers were gradually converted into open sewers where even the mighty courage of the salmon failed. The filth of thoughtless humanity has been the means of expelling this splendid creature from many of the rivers of its birthright.

The spring arrival of the salmon at the head of tide coincided with the spawning period of another anadromous fish, little silver smelts that came up from the Gulf of St Lawrence in millions to spawn in the river. Their journey took them no further than the fresh-water reaches where the tide eased. There they met the starving salmon, and died in millions in the well-formed teeth of the oceanbound wanderers. Then gorged with this first gift which the sea had sent to meet them, they came at last to the brackish taste of the rising tide, and as they moved into it the scent and taste of the brine became too strong for their unconditioned senses and they swirled away in confusion. Considerable readjustment was needed before they could penetrate into this strange new element. They settled for a while, cautious and careful in restless uncertainty, but even in their fearful suspicions, tantalising thrills of excitement continually swept over them and kept their long snouts pointing towards the ever-moving tide. In some strange way they realised that beyond the veil of filth lay the clean ocean wonderland of their dreams, a world for which their worn out sluggish bodies craved, for every member of the shoal had spent at least six months fasting in the river, and many of the spring salmon had spent a full year in fresh water.

Hunting parties continually broke away from the main shoal to chase the spawn-laden smelts, and the chases often ended in shallow water where the small fish sought sanctuary from the silvery monsters who hunted with the savagery of sharks. The tumult and splashing was heard by folk who dwelt near the river's edge and they knew that the mended kelts were dropping back.

For several days they drifted up and down the river

at the brackish head of every tide, and all the while the yearning to break into the sea grew ever stronger.

Once more it was the big hen who after her several journeys through the two elements, first entered the salty veil and headed into the steadily thickening darkness of the muddy water, and the schools of salmon followed her again. Gradually the taste of salt grew stronger, their hunger was quickened, and in spite of the foulness of the water, the omnipresent taste of the sea increased. Gradually revitalising strength came back to help them on their long last swim into the freedom of their natural element. The trap-net season had not yet opened along the banks of the estuary as they passed on in freedom of that hazard which had stopped so many on the way in. Now it was only the harbour seals and the hunting porpoises which would await their coming, and further out, the sharks, dolphins, and the grey seals of the Gulf, and the small killer whales of the northern ocean, and the endless hordes of harp seals whose numbers are beyond imagination. All these at their appointed places in the sea, would take their toll of the eager kelts from the rivers of New Brunswick as they would forge ahead to a secret rendezvous with the ocean of rebirth.

The big hen held the lead against the incoming tide, tailing her way steadily through several miles of the weakening scent of the Missimi below the towns until at last the pressure of the tide flow eased away between the ever-widening banks. Gradually the gloom in the water thinned and as the wanderers swept along the time honoured swim-ways of the estuary, the freedom of the sea called to them in the sound of waves breaking on the sandbar at the river's mouth. Suddenly prawns and sand eels lay before them, and they became flashing bars of silver as they started feeding among the Irish moss. Then steadily they moved out into the ever-deepening blue of the clear waters of the bay, and on and on towards the secret rejuvenation of all spent salmon where no man can follow, where feasting and the great renaissance of their lives could begin all over again.